GREAT YORKSHIRE

A CELEBRATION OF 150 SHOWS

EDITED BY DAVID JOY

FOREWORD BY H.R.H. THE PRINCE OF WALES

YORKSHIRE POST

GREAT NORTHERN

Great Northern Books Limited
PO Box 213, Ilkley, LS29 9WS

www.greatnorthernbooks.co.uk

© Great Northern Books 2008

Text: David Joy, Hilary Bowman and Tricia Johnson
Photographs: Yorkshire Post Newspapers, Yorkshire
Agricultural Society and other sources as per caption credits.

ISBN: 978 1 905080 44 1

Design and layout: David Burrill

Printed in Germany

CIP Data

A catalogue for this book is available from the British Library

CONTENTS

Foreword   5

Introduction   7

150 Shows   8

A Permanent Home   *photographic section*   24

Royal Occasions   *photographic section*   30

'The Show of Shows' -- Christopher Hall   36

'Massively more professional' – Bill Cowling   40

'A very good balance' – Chris Coleman   45

All Creatures Great and Small   *photographic section*   50

'The Show is healthier than ever' – Nick Lane Fox   60

'Once you get the farming community together it's fantastic' – Lady Ingilby   64

'Very pleasant memories' – Bert Verity   68

Action!   *photographic section*   74

'I would miss the Great Yorkshire hugely' – Margaret Chapman   84

'The competition is always hot' – David Broome   88

'The only show I would always go to' – Tricia Johnson   90

Dressed for the Day   *photographic section*   94

'One of the foremost shearing venues' – Bob Richardson   102

'A source of trusted information' – Jayne Hickinbotham   106

'It's always the pigs that have interested me' – Peter Brier   111

From Top to Toe   *photographic section*   116

Attendance and Entries   124

Leading Yorkshire families have strongly supported the show from the outset. Despite such generosity, this champion Hereford bull seemed unimpressed and was studiously ignoring the Queen's cousin Lord Harewood at a presentation ceremony in 2004.

CLARENCE HOUSE

As the Patron of the Yorkshire Agricultural Society, it gives me the greatest possible pleasure to send my warmest good wishes to the Society on their 150th Show.

Agriculture has changed beyond all recognition since the Show first began, but there are some things that have remained constant. The remarkable spirit of the Yorkshire farmers, the beauty of the land for which they care and their commitment to quality. The Great Yorkshire Show has been their showcase for generations and it is as important today as it was in 1838 – when the first Show was held. The role of the Show in linking consumers with producers, educating the public in how food is grown and spreading good practice amongst farmers while celebrating some of the finest livestock - and equestrianism - is crucial.

My visits to the Show have always given me the greatest possible pleasure, not least because of the warmth of the welcome I and my wife have received. The Great Yorkshire Show is not only a wonderfully Yorkshire occasion; it is also a very special national institution and I can only wish you a very happy 150th Show and send you all my heartfelt best wishes for the next one hundred and fifty...

Spectators enjoy some rodeo-style horse racing at the 91st Great Yorkshire Show at Halifax in 1939. Within two months the country would be at war, and there may well have been foreboding that this could be the last show for a long time. In the event it was another ten years before the Great Yorkshire was back in business with an event at Wakefield in 1949.

INTRODUCTION

The Great Yorkshire Show is without equal. One of the most prestigious and attractive of all agricultural shows, it presents the very best of British farming and food along with a unique mix of entertainment and competition. It manages at one and the same time to educate, demonstrate, inform and inspire.

Shows can be exhausting – and so can books about them. In order to give ample variety, this celebration of 150 shows is a mix of three very different themes. It begins with a broad look at the show from the birth of the organisers, the Yorkshire Agricultural Society in 1837 through to the present day. Key personalities associated with the Great Yorkshire then explain what the show means to them and why it is so very special. Interspersed with these accounts are scores of truly fascinating photographs that capture the essence of Yorkshire's premier event.

So large is today's Great Yorkshire that the content of this book has to be selective and inevitably tends to place the emphasis on livestock. There is much else at the show that is not quite as photogenic, and areas such as forestry, renewable energy, food and flowers should be on the 'must see' list of every visitor. As with the event as a whole, you will come away eager to re-visit what has been described as 'one of the greatest shows on earth'.

ACKNOWLEDGEMENTS

A special thanks to Hilary Bowman, as without her unstinting help a book that was little more than an idea in February 2008 could not have been completed in time to celebrate the 150th show. Thanks also to Deborah Goodall, Judy Thompson and Sally Wall in the Marketing & PR Department of the Yorkshire Agricultural Society. Tricia Johnson and Robert Benson, agricultural correspondent of the Yorkshire Post, provided valuable background information, and without exception the personalities who have contributed to the book could not have been more helpful. Naming names is invidious, but Bert Verity in his 95th year was amazing!

Useful sources have been Professor Vince Hall's A History of the Yorkshire Agricultural Society 1837 - 1987 *and the files of the Yorkshire Post.*

David Joy, April 2008

150 SHOWS

A brief moment of glorious infamy for the Black Caterpillar has long gone. It happened at the very first Yorkshire Show in 1838 when the creature had gained such notoriety that a report on its 'ravages' gained a special prize of £5. It was unquestionably a generous sum (the equivalent of about £215 in today's money), the same amount no doubt also being gratefully received by agricultural labourer Alexander Kiddy, age 82. Extraordinary as it may now seem, his reward was for bringing up the greatest number of children without having to resort to financial help from his parish. His tally was fourteen. So it went on, with a more substantial sum of £10 being handed out to the best turnip-soil farm and a further £10 for the best cultivation on a farm with stony land.

Quaint by today's standards, it all reflected the zeal of the new Victorian age that was just dawning. English agriculture was at last emerging from a prolonged depression brought on by the after effects of the Napoleonic wars. Livestock production was dramatically on the increase and there was an adequate supply of ready capital to finance further expansion. It was in such circumstances that a gathering of the great and the good took place at the Black Swan Hotel in York on 10 October 1837. The upshot was the formation of the Yorkshire Agricultural Society, with the object of arranging 'an annual meeting for the exhibition of farming stock, implements, etc, and for the general promotion of agriculture'. The prestigious event was to be held successively in different places in the county on the last Wednesday in August each year, the first meeting to take place in York in August 1838.

The stage was thus firmly set, the vision being ably guided through to reality by the Society's first president, the third Earl Spencer. The cousin of Queen Victoria, he was an active statesman but more importantly was also a leading livestock breeder who was immensely respected by farmers. Previously Viscount Althorp, he displayed the family trait of not being afraid to be outspoken. He once invited a rather pretentious Duke to a meeting at the Smithfield Club in London and told him: 'We dine at the Crown & Anchor, like farmers in boots!' When he succeeded to the earldom and retired from politics, it was reported that he 'thereafter kept company with the creatures he most respected – his Shorthorns, his sheep and the farming community'.

Helping to put the Society on a firm footing were many of the leading figures in

The October 1837 report in the Leeds Mercury announcing the formation of the Yorkshire Agricultural Society. It was charged with arranging annual exhibitions in different places in the county, which proved to be the forerunners of today's Great Yorkshire Show.

Bramham, Oct. 9, 1837.   B. EAMONSON.

YORKSHIRE AGRICULTURAL SOCIETY.— On Tuesday last, an important meeting of noblemen and gentry connected with agriculture in this county, was held at the Black Swan Hotel, York, by adjournment from a previous meeting held on the 29th of August last, when it was determined to form a society, to be entitled the Yorkshire Agricultural Society. Among the gentry present on the occasion were, Earl Spencer, Earl de Grey, Lord Huntingfield, Hon. Sir E. M. Vavasour, Bart., of Hazlewood Hall ; Hon. C. Langdale, of Holme ; Sir F. L. Wood, Bart., of Hemsworth ; Sir J. V. B. Johnstone, Bart. of Hackness ; G. L. Fox, Esq. M.P., of Bramham Park ; J. W. Childers, Esq., M.P., of Cantley ; W. R. C. Stansfield, Esq., M.P., of Esholt ; J. S. Crompton, Esq., M.P. of Woodend ; P. B. Thompson, Esq., of Escrick Park ; W. B. Wrightson, Esq. M.P., of Cudworth ; J. Walker, Esq., of Sand Hutton ; W. Busfield, Esq., M.P. of Upwood ; Mark Foulis, Esq., of Heslerton ; T. Duncombe, Esq. of Copgrove ; A. Empson, Esq., of Blacktoft ; F. Cholmeley, Esq., of Bransby ; Henry Preston, Esq., of Moreby ; Capt. Dowker, of Huntington ; H. S. Thompson, Esq., of Fairfield ; W. M. Hatfeild, Esq. of Newton Kyme ; Rev. T. Harrison, of Firby ; Wm. Allen, Esq., of Malton ; W. Donkin, Esq of Westow Hall ; Godfrey Wentworth, Esq. of Woolley Park ; Richard Fleetwood Shaw, Esq. of Brantingham Thorpe; R. Denison, Esq., of Kilnwick ; — Tempest, Esq.; Mr. Alderman Hudson, of York ; H. Smithson, Esq., of Malton ; T. Barstow, Esq., of Garrow Hill ; James Barber, Esq., of Tanghall ; T. Price, Esq. of Clementhorpe ; R. Hey, Esq., of York, &c. &c. On the motion of R. DENISON Esq., it was resolved that Earl Spencer be requested to take the chair. The resolutions and a list of the subscribers will be found in our second page.

HUDDERSFIELD BOROUGH REGISTRATION.

Yorkshire agriculture. They included George Lane Fox of Bramham Park, whose descendant Nick Lane Fox is still closely associated with the show and contributes to this book. A less auspicious name, buried towards the foot of the long list in the Leeds Mercury report, was 'Mr Alderman Hudson of York'. He was perhaps rightly regarded as an upstart, as this was the infamous 'railway king', George Hudson, whose corrupt business practices were to precipitate his spectacular downfall twelve years later.

The first show, held in the Barrack Yard of the 5th Dragoons on the outskirts of York, proved to be a spectacular success. Earl Spencer arrived on the Monday and personally supervised the erection of livestock pens as well as ensuring that stewards were provided with bands and white rosettes. Most of the show-animals were brought in on the Tuesday with due pomp and ceremony, great excitement being created by Earl Carlisle's large caravan of two fine oxen drawn by four grey horses and Lord Dundas's enormous bull that fortunately was 'securely fixed on a wooden wagon'.

On the Wednesday the whole area took on the festivity of a fair. The two gates – one for Society members and the other for the 'ordinary public' -– were opened promptly at twelve o' clock. Ironically, it was the members who let the side down, as by two o' clock the pressure against their gate was so great that it burst asunder and several hundred people streamed in without tickets. A scuffle ensued between the crowd and the soldiers and police, who were 'obliged to use their sticks, the blows of which were returned'.

Order was soon restored and, even though it was little more than a half-day event, the show netted receipts of £244 (£10,500 today) and boosted membership of the Society to around the 800 mark. The Yorkshire Gazette enthusiastically noted that 'the show of stallions was the finest which we have ever witnessed', the cattle were 'admirable in point and symmetry', the display of sheep was 'equal to anything ever seen before', and 'the monster pigs were viewed with admiration and astonishment'. The day ended in style with a Great Dinner, attended by almost a thousand people. Reflecting the nineteenth century love of lengthy oratory, it included some sixteen speeches with much being said about the importance of manure to the small farmer.

The way was now clear to forge ahead with the original aims of mounting an annual show that toured the county. Leeds was selected as the venue in 1839 and then Northallerton and Hull. It was back to York in 1842, which was the first year that attendance was recorded with a modest total of 6,044. From the following year the event became known as the Great Yorkshire Show, apparently by popular acclaim rather than official edict. There was something uniquely Yorkshire about the reasoning that this nullified the need for a royal charter. It was held that it would oblige the title 'Royal Yorkshire Show' to be used, which would be less distinctive than the 'Great'!

Any differences of opinion on this subject were put to one side when the Royal

Agricultural Society of England and the Yorkshire Agricultural Society joined forces to stage a one-off show at York in 1848. It proved to be another great success, in part due to the spacious 180-acre [73 hectare] site on Bootham Stray. Close to the new York to Scarborough railway, it allowed branch lines to be laid directly into the showground. It was probably the greatest display of agricultural implements ever organised, the working trials involving four days of exhausting judging from Friday to Monday. On the Saturday the judges were working until 11.0pm and on the Monday they started at 4.0am. The Implements Yard was open to the public on the Tuesday with a relatively modest admission charge of 2s 6d (about £5 today). There was a huge attendance on the Wednesday when Prince Albert arrived to see the show, while the final day saw agricultural labourers turning up in large numbers to 'have a real good look at the implements'.

Thereafter the Great Yorkshire settled back to its normal roving routine. The years from 1850 to 1875 have been described as 'the golden age of agriculture' and it is thus not surprising that the show became a two-day event in 1853. The demand for 'more' continued and after just another nine years the present three-day format was successfully adopted. In the 1860s a specific rotation was

The hugely successful event in 1848 when the Great Yorkshire and Royal Shows jointly put on a week-long extravaganza in York. The upper engraving shows the immense cattle and implement sheds erected on Bootham Stray, and at top left one of the branch railways specially built for the occasion. In the centre of the lower picture is the elaborate pavilion provided for the show dinner, with the familiar landmark of Clifford's Tower and the now demolished prison walls on its right.

THE CATTLE AND IMPLEMENT SHEDS.

THE ROYAL AGRICULTURAL SOCIETY'S MEETING AT YORK.—THE DINNER PAVILION, FROM THE NEW-WALK.—(SEE PAGE 32.)

[COUNTRY EDITION.]

Standing in the centre of this group is John Hannam, a land agent based at Kirk Deighton, near Wetherby, who was appointed as secretary of the Yorkshire Agricultural Society in 1854. He resigned nine years later after it was alleged that he had retained a substantial sum of money belonging to the Society.

The men responsible for the Great Yorkshire's first hound show in 1859, when Hull was the chosen venue.

agreed with the 1866 show at York and thence in succeeding years at locations in the North Riding, the northern half of the West Riding, the East Riding and the southern half of the West Riding. The cycle then resumed at York, this broad pattern continuing until the onset of hard times towards the end of the century. Within this framework there was intense competition from individual towns and cities to secure the show. For example, in 1853 both Ripon and York had offered a sum of £300, a large field for the showground, a separate field and sufficient horses for the implements trial and a dining room for two hundred. The outcome was presumably satisfactory on all sides, as the show went first to York and then to Ripon the following year.

HIGH NOON

There is nothing better than the fulsome columns of a local newspaper in the heyday of Victorian England for capturing the atmosphere of an event such as the Great Yorkshire Show. The Yorkshire Gazette rose splendidly to the occasion in 1860 when it covered its first and only visit to Pontefract:

'This morning the trains from various parts, and omnibuses, cabs and numerous other vehicles brought large numbers of persons to Pontefract. The town from an early hour presented a scene of gaiety and rejoicing, the streets generally being festooned right across with garlands of flowers and evergreens, and from the windows of the houses were suspended flags and banners of all descriptions.

'In the first place we will speak of the implement yard. Great interest was manifestly felt by the visitors who inspected the vast array of agricultural mechanism which invited their attention on every hand. There was a continual noise kept up in this

department throughout the day. The steam engines were at work puffing and blowing away, and the thrashing machines were in full operation displaying their useful capacities, their monotonous buzz and hum falling not very pleasantly upon the ear without a moment's cessation. The turnip and straw cutters ad infinitum were worked from time to time. But the most attractive object in the implement field was the gigantic and powerful brick moulding and pressing machine of Messrs Bradley and Craven, of Wakefield, which was at work today and attracted crowds of spectators.

'The display of short-horned cattle next claims our attention. The bulls of any age, seven in number, were a fine lot and when they were brought into the ring to undergo the ordeal of the judges, their symmetrical proportions were seen to advantage by visitors who stood around the circle. The cow and heifer classes were of a superior description, and fully sustained the reputation of Yorkshire for cattle breeding.

'In sheep, the traits of fine blood and quality were discernible in every class. The shearling rams numbered twenty-four, certainly a large entry, and the competition for the prizes was most severe indeed.

'We next come to the pigs, which were in the primest condition possible, the boars and sows of the large breed fully justifying the truth of the name applied to them, for they were really of gigantic growth, and with respect to the porcine tribe as a whole brought together on the showground they could not be excelled.'

The tradition of the Great Dinner started in 1838 had continued and this was covered in equally ponderous style. In order to allow time for the numerous speeches, it began at 5.0pm and included toasts to the Queen, the Prince Consort and the rest of the Royal Family, the Army and the Navy, the Yorkshire Agricultural Society and 'the labouring classes'. In accordance with protocol this was a men-only event, but 'a large number of ladies were admitted to the gallery to witness the dinner and hear the speeches'. Quite what they thought of starving as others feasted is not recorded, nor is their reaction to the toast 'The ladies'. As no females were formally present, a gallant gentleman had to respond on their behalf!

The ladies may have felt slightly happier the following day: 'A vast concourse of persons was assembled and they were enabled to promenade to their heart's content through the showground. There were choice specimens of the human species to look out for: the noblemen, clergy and gentlemen of the county – the Earls Cathcart and Harewood, the Lords Galway, Herries, Middleton and Wenlock, most members of the Council and Reverends galore.'

UPS AND DOWNS

If there were indeed a golden age of agriculture, it ended spectacularly for the Great Yorkshire Show with a dazzling performance at Sheffield in 1874. Attendance at 64,111 was almost double that of any previous show. Receipts soared to £4,500 and were instrumental in turning in a profit of £700 (approaching £30,000 at today's values). A belief that nothing could stop an even greater profit stemming from further expansion unfortunately proved to be ill founded. Agricultural depression from the mid-1870s was made worse by disastrously bad weather and attendance at the 1875 show in Driffield was a dismal 27,149. The following year's show at Skipton was even worse, with all three days a washout, and in 1877 the Society was suddenly faced with running an overdraft to keep the event afloat.

Matters then fluctuated until disaster finally struck at the dawn of the new century

in 1900. It was the turn of the Royal Show to be held in York and hitherto it had been the custom not to mount the Great Yorkshire on such occasions. In this fateful year a powerful deputation from Doncaster offered such strong enticements to hold the show in the town that the Society was persuaded to go ahead. It overruled the objections of a minority, who prophetically argued that the economic conditions of the farming community would not support two major shows in the county within a month of each other. The result was catastrophic, the total attendance of a mere 20,193 being the lowest for more than thirty years. The event lost some £3,000, which today would be in excess of £150,000. A resolution was swiftly passed that there was no justification for holding another show until the funds of the Society were placed on a sounder basis. It was begging-bowl time.

It says much for the generosity of Yorkshire folk and the high regard in which the show was held that the response was magnificent. In less than a year the Society was back on its feet and the 1901 event at Bradford went ahead virtually as normal. Yet the debacle did trigger a feeling among some members that the whole concept of a peripatetic show, faced with the constant costs of moving from one venue to another, was fatally flawed. Calls were made for a permanent showground, and telling arguments produced that this would save a vast amount of time, money and crippling anxiety, but it was to be another half century before these were finally accepted.

In the meantime the show expanded on all fronts and enjoyed a great revival in the optimistic spirit of the Edwardian age. The attendance of 82,461 at Bradford in 1914 was the largest ever recorded and forty-two years would pass before it was exceeded. It was a landmark that triggered numerous hopes and aspirations, but these were all suddenly

The spacious grounds of Temple Newsam, near Leeds, proved ideal for the 1932 show. Visitors would be able to tour the mansion in the background, first built by Thomas Lord Darcy, who was executed by Henry VIII. It was purchased by Leeds Corporation in 1922 for use as a museum.

extinguished by the outbreak of war. A decision on whether to hold a show in 1915 was in fact initially deferred for the apparent reason that it was thought the conflict would be a temporary affair. There was an irrefutable logic to the ultimate decision not to proceed. The Society felt unable to estimate the cost of holding the show under wartime conditions but could easily calculate the cost of the event not taking place. As the latter alternative entailed no risk, whereas the former would be enormously hazardous, it was therefore decided to cancel.

It was assumed in 1919 that it would be an easy task to hold a triumphant show at York as part of a victory celebration. The reality was quite otherwise, as preliminary estimates showed that costs of labour and raw materials had risen so formidably as to be financially crippling. Only when a thorough review had put the Society on a new footing to face new times was it considered feasible to put on a show at Leeds in 1921. Matters then quickly improved, culminating in the 1926 event on Harrogate's famous Stray, which was considered to be 'unquestionably the most successful in the history of the Society'. Attracting a gate of 52,845, it left a surplus of £3,840. A remarkably full programme was prepared for all three days, essentially similar to that of today, although less varied and less tilted

The impressive show at York in 1937 marked the centenary of the Yorkshire Agricultural Society. On the right is the vast display of farm implements mounted by the famous manufacturer Ransomes, Sims & Jefferies Ltd of Ipswich. This photograph gives a good impression of the broad board walks that were such a feature in the days prior to a permanent showground.

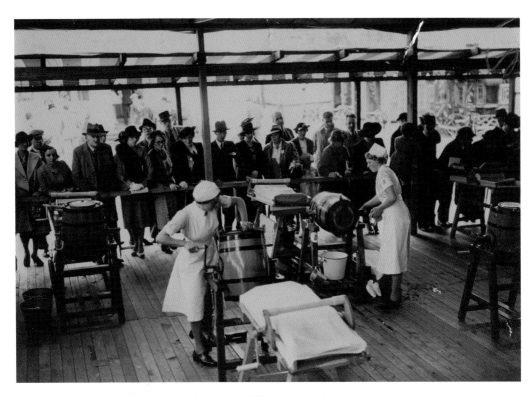

Dairymaids 1930s' style. A demonstration at the 1938 Doncaster show.

towards pure entertainment. Princess Mary attended, her husband Viscount Lascelles being that year's president. Livestock entries were an amazing 1,650 in excess of any previous show, the event as a whole re-kindling calls for a permanent showground based at Harrogate.

The programme was indicative of the times: 'The Members' Dining Room is provided for the use of Members and their friends. Admission by Badge only (admitting one Lady also) provided there is room. The Members' Reading and Writing Room, and Lady Members' Room adjoining, with lavatory accommodation, etc, [are] in the centre of the Show Yard.'

Despite the difficult economic times, the Society now grew increasingly affluent and in 1937 was in a strong position to commemorate its centenary with a spectacular event on the 50 acres [20 hectares] of York Knavesmire – widely considered to be one of the best show sites in Britain. The Yorkshire Gazette struck a timely note that still holds good some seventy years later, commenting that the show 'covered every department of rural life, and did much to provide the bridge over the gulf between the interests of town and country, which is agriculture's crying need today'.

The Princess Royal became the Society's first lady president and proved remarkably active in that role, chairing the General Meeting and personally delivering the annual address on the showground. The speech at a press luncheon was given by Lord Middleton,

The show at Malton in 1950 proved the last of the 'roaming' events that had been part of the Great Yorkshire's existence for well over a century. The 'Rural Industries' stand very much reflected the design ideology of the day.

who certainly had an eye for headlines: 'What would our forebears of 1837 say of our stock? I think that they would be pleased with our cattle, sheep and pigs, but they might question our wisdom in producing much of our breeding stock at the show in disgustingly fat condition. They would criticise our cart horses for being too big and coarse, and say that our hunters are too much like racehorses.'

He ended by posing some questions to which he probably had a shrewd idea of the answers: 'One wonders just what the future holds. Whether the changes from 1937 to 2037 will be as sharp as the changes from 1837 to 1937. I suppose that all the machinery of today will be museum pieces in fifty years' time. Will horses on the land survive for another century or will they disappear?'

Change soon came with a vengeance, the 1939 show at Halifax proving to be the last for more than a decade. This time there was no hesitation in closing down for the duration of the war, the difficult conditions immediately afterwards meaning that it was 1949 before Wakefield became the venue for the first post-war show. The breathing space, coupled with continuing uncertainty, led to another revival of calls for a permanent showground.

This time there was no going back, although there was much initial wavering between York and Harrogate as the best location. In the end a 200-acre [80 hectare] site, overlooking Rudding Park on the outskirts of Harrogate, was purchased for £16,500.

Aerial view of the Great Yorkshire's Harrogate showground with the superb main ring conspicuous in the centre. The livestock sheds are in the foreground.

A HOME OF ITS OWN — AFTER 113 YEARS!

It was a milestone when in 1951 the Great Yorkshire Show became the first in the country to settle on a fixed site. All was ready in time for the inaugural event, one difference from today being that much of the livestock was brought north from that year's Royal Show at Cambridge by special trains rather than by road. Although it was a new era the facilities remained the traditional mixture of canvas and timber accommodation, as developing the showground was a massive undertaking destined to take over fifteen years. At first there were formidable difficulties with steel and timber on licence, cement virtually unobtainable and special permission needed to build anything larger than a dog kennel. There was no architect or surveyor, and models were made of the layout with individual structures being shunted around until the balance was considered right. Work on £50,000 worth of buildings was about to start in September 1951 when the Chancellor of the Exchequer imposed a ban on all new construction for five months.

Gradually matters improved and work

Blessed with its own purpose-built exhibition hall, the Flower Show has become an eagerly anticipated and virtually self-contained event within the Great Yorkshire Show. Here is a smiling Andy Hubbuck of Chesterfield, winner of the sweet pea competition in 2005.

got underway on such core projects as the main ring. A determination that it should quite simply be the finest in the country necessitated the removal of 60,000 tons of soil to level the site, but when completed in 1955 there was no doubt as to the value of this massive undertaking. Another landmark project took much longer to bring to fruition. By now the Flower Show had become a hugely popular part of the Great Yorkshire, stimulating a need for its own exhibition hall, but it was not finally completed until 1967 due to design and cost problems.

Responsible for seeing through most of the construction was works superintendent Charles Dickinson. Apart from the main ring itself, he supervised the building of the associated grandstand 180 metres long and nine metres high, as well as what were claimed to be the biggest cattle sheds in Europe with accommodation for seven hundred beasts as well as bedrooms for the stockmen and offices for the breed societies. He was known by members as 'the man who never panics', a quality shared by those such as Dave Robinson, Ken Bell and Dave Atkinson who look after the showground today and collectively have given amazing longevity of service.

The investment made in the new showground back in 1951 soon reaped its reward in terms of attendance, which soared through most of the 1950s. A six-figure gate was achieved for the first time on the occasion of the one-hundredth show in 1957, when a hitherto unimaginable total of 118,593 men, women and children poured through the turnstiles. There were still difficult patches, notably in the early 1970s when poor trade bookings coupled with a soaring overdraft led to a serious proposal that the showground be sold. It was defeated but only after some heated debate that culminated in management changes and some welcome innovation. A common complaint that there was never anything new at the Great Yorkshire was now countered and the 1974 show set the trend. It included an 'Adventure in Yorkshire' exhibition with a steam engine, a model of the Humber Bridge, a display of 'Public Transport through the Ages' and helicopter rides that proved very popular with children. Also helping to draw in the crowds were such events as a working terrier show, a demonstration of rare breeds of cattle and competitions for horse shoeing, sheep shearing and even chainsaw carving.

The new and more energetic approach quickly paid dividends. Just as in the dawn of the twentieth century, recovery from hard times was swift and throughout the late 1970s the show went from strength to strength, culminating in 1979 with a record 131,075 people paying over £250,000 to come through the gate. Figures tailed off in the harsher economic climate of the 1990s, although the emphasis was deliberately put on the quality of the show as much as the sheer weight of numbers. All was going well until 2001, when disaster suddenly struck. The Yorkshire Post of 1 June carried the front-page headline: 'Great Yorkshire Show is axed as crisis continues'.

Charles Dickinson, who was responsible for much of the building work on the showground.

Readers needed no reminding of the nature of the crisis, which was stalking the land with horrific consequences, but it was spelt out in graphic detail: 'Foot-and-Mouth claimed one of Yorkshire's most prestigious events yesterday when the Great Yorkshire Show was cancelled for the first time in half a century. Organisers of the show – the region's premier agricultural showcase, which costs £1.4m to stage and attracts more than 120,000 people – announced the cancellation as four more cases of foot-and-mouth were confirmed at farms in the Skipton area. The news came forty-eight hours after the National Farmers' Union declared it was pulling out of the show. Regional information officer Rob Simpson said last night: "The

The queue winds into the far distance as some of the then record crowd of 128,487 wait patiently to get into the showground in 1964. The cars and the cigarette advertising all help to date this now period scene.

Great Yorkshire Show is traditionally one of the highlights of the agricultural calendar in Yorkshire and is the premier show in the North. This is a major blow, not just for the rural community but also for the morale of the farming community in Yorkshire. What has happened is symptomatic of the ravages that foot-and-mouth has caused to the rural economy."'

There could have been no greater setback, as a few months earlier the omens for an outstanding show were truly in the ascendant with entries high and the Queen and the Duke of Edinburgh due to attend on the first day. Yet it is an old adage that out of adversity can come strength, and sheer determination to forge ahead was evident in the 2002 show with its highest attendance for more than twenty years. The momentum has been maintained and the gate for subsequent years has never dropped below the 120,000 mark.

The sun smiled on the righteous in 2007 when appalling weather forced the cancellation of many similar events including the Game Fair and the Royal Show. It seemed at one stage that the Great Yorkshire might go the same way, but then the clouds parted and £70,000 spent on improving ground conditions saved the day.

No longer is the showground just the preserve of the Great Yorkshire Show. A second annual event, Countryside Live, has become well established and a host of other fixtures mean that in excess of a million visitors are now welcomed every year. The mere six thousand who formed the first recorded attendance when they trooped into the York show in 1842 would be dumbfounded.

Sign of the times in 2001, when Foot and Mouth disease forced the cancellation of the Great Yorkshire Show for the first time apart from war years and their aftermath.

'THEY HAVE GOT IT JUST RIGHT'

Thirty years ago the Yorkshire Post agricultural correspondent, Robert Benson, echoed the views of many when he commented that the show's farming flavour was being sacrificed in favour of a desire to get people thought the gate. He concluded: 'Before the rot goes any further, the Yorkshire officials must maintain what agricultural interest there still remains, and go some way towards building on this as soon as possible. How far should they go is the million-dollar question. It would be interesting to hear how farmers feel about the show – whether they go in order to learn something or whether they are merely taking their families for a day out. But if the Society fails to maintain what agricultural interest is still left, then to my mind it should no longer use the word "Great" in its show title.'

The report set the cat among the pigeons but Robert Benson has no regrets. He feels that some aspects of the show were then reminiscent of Blackpool pleasure beach. Today he takes a very different view: 'The show strikes a superb balance between entertainment and serious agriculture. It does much to educate the public on how farming works and is infinitely better at promoting food and local produce. In the past it was simply the judging of animals, as though they had nothing to do with food. At the same time the Great Yorkshire stands very high in the estimation of farmers. It is a fine balancing act but now they have got it just right.'

A PERMANENT HOME

A fascinating collection of photographs survives from 1954, soon after the Great Yorkshire moved to its permanent showground at Harrogate. This selection shows how some features have since changed almost out of recognition, while others seem remarkably familiar today.

Attendance in 1954 was 80,508, the highest for more than a quarter of a century, but still relatively small compared with recent figures. The showground seems relatively quiet, but it could be that everyone is clustered together with eyes firmly on the main ring.

The grand parade of cattle was then as now a major focus of attention.

Some of the most noticeable changes over the last half-century have been in the field of agricultural machinery. The tractors in this picture seem tiny in comparison with today's monsters.

The sun was shining brightly when this photograph was taken, but it clearly shows one of the surfaced avenues that in wet weather were a massive improvement over the wooden walkways of the earlier showgrounds.

We don't know what they are all watching, but it is certainly the subject of serious attention. Note that nearly everyone has a hat and a tie as well as polished shoes. It is clearly still largely a man's world!

Health & Safety might today have a word or two to say about some of the working practices evident in this picture, but there is no doubt that the circular saw and logging machine are creating considerable interest.

The parade of heavy horses drew a large crowd in 1954 just as it does today.

Everyone pays attention as the diameter of a sawn section of a tree is carefully measured.

Waiting patiently in 'Sheep Ring No 2: Lincoln'.

Keeping young children occupied was clearly appreciated at the new showground from the outset. A remarkable amount of sand appears to be still in the sandpit!

ROYAL OCCASIONS

The Royal family has long been a strong supporter of the Great Yorkshire Show and has honoured the event with their presence on many occasions. These photographs depict just some of the many royal visits over the last seventy-five years.

The Duke and Duchess of York at the 1932 Show, held in Leeds.

Princess Elizabeth at Wakefield in 1949. This was the first Great Yorkshire Show since the event at Halifax in 1939.

The Queen and Mr M H Tollet's mare Silverin, ridden by Harry Bonner. The occasion was the 1957 Hunter Championship.

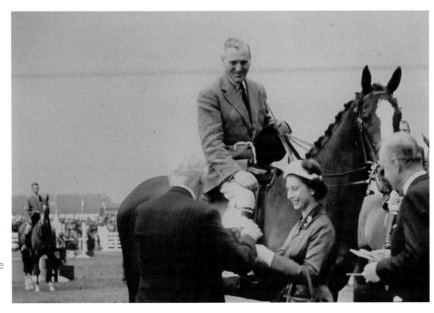

The Queen looking happy and relaxed when she visited the Show during her two-day Silver Jubilee tour of Yorkshire in 1977.

A prize-winning bull was on its best behaviour for Princess Margaret in 1982.

The 150th anniversary of the Yorkshire Agricultural Society in 1987 was commemorated with a visit by the Duchess of Kent. On the left is the Marquis of Normanby (President) and on the right Major General G de E Collin (Show Director). Behind them is Mr F K Abbey (Chief Steward of Cattle).

Princess Anne, the Princess Royal, driven by Mr A C P Wharton and accompanied by Mr A T Preston (Show Director) in 1992.

The Duke of York is clearly in jovial mood in 2002 but the Bald-Headed Eagle seems a little uncertain on how to respond.

The Prince of Wales has strong links with the Great Yorkshire Show in his capacity as Patron. Here he is in 1999, seemingly sharing a joke with Judy Bell, chair of Yorkshire Pantry.

The Prince of Wales was back in 2006, accompanied by the Duchess of Cornwall. Wearing badges saying 'I am a Great British Farmer', they are seen here at close quarters with an Ayrshire cow.

The Prince and the Duchess were presented with a matching pair of shepherds' crooks made by Wensleydale farmer William Lambert. Prince Charles carried his crook throughout his four-hour visit to the Show, which attracted a record attendance of 135,111.

'THE SHOW OF SHOWS'
CHRISTOPHER HALL

President of the Society in 2007-2008, Christopher Hall was Honorary Show Director from 1998-2005. On his land at Eavestone, on the side of the eastern Pennines, he and his wife Jackie keep horses and let their land to a local sheep and cattle farmer.

One of the reasons for the horses is that I am also Master of the West of Yore Hunt. My wife is also a keen member and sometimes whips-in, so we're very much involved with hunting. Since I retired from being the Show Director, that takes up all our time.

When I was a child my parents were members of the Yorkshire Agricultural Society. My family were leather tanners in York in a very old business that started in 1780 and was sold in the 1950s and my father then went from doing that to farming; dairy and arable. I decided I would do my own thing and I had a career supplying systems to the printing industry.

One of my earliest memories of the show was going with my mother and father, but principally my mother, into the members' enclosure where all the ladies were dressed in their finery, including hats. Maybe not as posh as Ascot – more county!

I always enjoyed looking at the livestock

Christopher Hall, photographed in 2005 when Show Director.

and the ponies and horses. I became a steward in the late seventies, early eighties, because of my involvement with horses and hunting. At that time I was also building up my own business.

One of the best aspects of the Great Yorkshire is always the comradeship of the other horse stewards, most of whom were involved somewhere in the equestrian world and principally in hunting so it was a very friendly team.

The standards have always remained very high – that is one of the principle features of the show – and while numbers have increased significantly over the years, I'm pleased to say the quality has been very much maintained. For example in showjumping, the Cock o' the North competition is still regarded as one of the principle showjumping competitions in the UK.

Also, from the competitors' point of view to win at the Great Yorkshire whether it is in a livestock section or stickmaking is an enormous honour as, without doubt, whatever the section, this show is considered to be the show of shows. The prestige that it carries is enormous and is very heavily competed for.

I became Show Director at a time that coincided with the sale of my business which was very appropriate for me because I'd been used to a very busy business life and, rather than retire, it gave me something which required a great deal of effort and energy. The Show Director is at the head of the organisation of the two Society shows that happen at Harrogate so suddenly I was faced with the position of being responsible for the Great Yorkshire Show and that was quite something!

Life of course never runs smoothly and at the beginning of 2001 came the dreaded information that Foot & Mouth disease had broken out. Initially after the outbreak, we

Christopher and Jackie Hall chat to Charlotte Gill, age 13, on Stanley Grange Roulette from Great Ayton. [2007]

tried hard to keep the show going but it eventually became clear that it wasn't in the interests of the farming industry for huge crowds to be gathered together in Harrogate and reluctantly therefore, we had to cancel.

Although this happened in the April, there was still a cost of over £1million that we couldn't recover and so it was a serious financial situation. I always say it was the industry and the competitors who were extremely keen on there being a Great Yorkshire Show that made starting up again in 2002 so much easier. We had tremendous support from everybody to have a show despite the fact that there wouldn't be so much livestock.

Everybody came in '02 absolutely determined that they were going to recover from Foot & Mouth. Bear in mind there were people who had been shut up in their farms for months and months and quite a number had lost their entire herd. So it was very critical that we had a show and it coincided with a visit from the Duke of York. He was very good in getting everybody together and so the '02 show, though it was smaller, was a wonderful recovery.

The Duke, unusually for a royal, was ahead of his schedule. Usually, the Show Director spends time trying to keep royals on time as they're very good, and are always going off the agenda talking to people but he was ahead of his schedule. I knew that if I got him to the main ring too early, it might be awkward. The main ring was the last call on his tour of the show and when we got there, the only thing that was happening was twenty-five blokes in yellow jackets with buckets and shovels shovelling up after the cattle parade which had finished ten minutes before. It was the longest quarter of an hour of my life trying to keep the Duke, who is very keen to learn and very much on the ball, interested while twenty-five blokes shovelled it into buckets.

One year we had problems with the water because vast amounts of water are used up during the course of the show and we'd got to the bottom of one of the holding tanks and the water had become muddy. One chap took his white alpaca to clean its feet, sprayed it with a hosepipe and it came out brown. He wasn't at all impressed but I think we managed to retrieve the situation.

The great success of the show is the livestock and I'd include horses in the livestock. The cattle and sheep are absolutely fundamental to the show because they come from proper farms and proper farmers. Perhaps the most important job that the Show Director has to do is to ensure that the show

is true to its agricultural heritage and of all of the major shows the Great Yorkshire has been the most successful in doing this. This means that above all the quality of exhibits whether livestock or something else has to be maintained and at the same time the truly agricultural content is always to the fore. We have also managed to maintain and increase the amount of trade stands that have a genuine rural connection.

The show has never been more popular than it is now. We've had record crowds or near record crowds in the last few years and that's because it is a platform for agriculture and all things rural. The public, even those from inner cities, have an enormous interest in what goes on in the country. That's why the Society's work has never been more topical and I can see that continuing as far into the future as anybody can envisage.

We are asked very many interesting questions. On our educational programme we have what we call Countryside Days in June when 5,000 schoolchildren come to a mini-show and we show them all aspects of rural life. Many of these children are from inner cities. To hear remarks like 'Cor, I never realised milk came from cows' or 'I've never been on long grass before' is so rewarding, it feels you really are achieving something. It happens at the show too. Lots of people are amazed at what they see.

Farming is still, thank God, very important in Yorkshire and we've been able to maintain the very high standards of exhibition at the show and that strikes a chord with the public who are extremely supportive of everything that we do.

I come out of office at the end of this year's Great Yorkshire Show but I'm sure I shall be a member until I'm no longer around. It's been an important period of time in my life and the fact that it strives for excellence all the time is something that's very important to me. I love things of quality that

Christopher Hall has seen many changes during his involvement with the Great Yorkshire Show. It was the end of an era when the Shire horse 'Royal', with Driver Dudley Parker, pulled the Tetley wagon round the main ring for the last time. [2006]

are worthwhile and the Society and the show are absolutely worthwhile.

One very important aspect is that much of the show organisation is due to volunteers, who give their time freely and with great enthusiasm, and that includes the stewards at the showground and also the network of committees. Every section has its own committee and all these people volunteer their time and effort and energy, right through to the trustees of the organisation who spend a great deal of their time over the year, and sometimes I forget to thank them all.

'MASSIVELY MORE PROFESSIONAL'
BILL COWLING

Honorary Show Director, Bill Cowling was handed the reins by predecessor Christopher Hall after the 2005 show. Bill and his wife Caroline farm at their 600-acre family farm at Pannal, south of Harrogate, looking after beef cattle, sheep and some arable land. Until two years ago, there was also a dairy herd. The farm is now mostly run by their elder son Tom, his wife Karen and their younger son Guy.

I was formerly the show's Chief Cattle Steward for about ten years and prior to that I had stewarded in the cattle section for fifteen years. The family used to show dairy cattle at the Great Yorkshire Show in the 1960s so I was involved with that.

My earliest memories of the show were when I was at school. I remember coming and looking round all the agricultural implements and machinery – and the cattle and sheep, of course. At that time I thought the huge tractors and combine harvesters were absolutely wonderful.

I suppose I started driving vehicles on the farm at home before it was probably legally allowed. In those days there weren't those sort of rules.

Literally three or four weeks after each year's show we start planning for the following year and through the autumn, in

Bill Cowling, Show Director. [2007]

September and October mostly, every section of the show has its own meeting; cattle, sheep, goats, rabbits, poultry, you name it. It involves about twenty-five different committees. The stewards and the people involved in those sections meet here at the showground and put forward ideas for the year's show and select the judges. They look at how the previous show went and how we could improve.

It's grown to be massively more 'professional' over the years, as have most other agricultural shows. From being very much a rural event and fairly relaxed, professionalism has come into the organisation of it. It's slicker and it's obviously much, much more expensive to stage because tentage and all these sort of things get more and more expensive, almost by the day, and the sophistication of both the exhibitors of livestock and the exhibitors of trade stands has grown.

One of the things we notice is the demand for electricity. In years gone by, a trade stand would have probably had a plug for a kettle and that would be about it. Now a lot of them are so sophisticated, they have air conditioning, refrigeration units so drinks are cold or heating units, so demand for electricity throughout the showground grows year on year. And of course the infrastructure that we have to have to deliver it also has to grow with it.

There are also computers to consider. Agriculture has grown more sophisticated and has become more dependent on technology… as has life. Gone are the days of pen and paper.

One of the great things that the Great Yorkshire Show has done, and probably better than some other agricultural societies, is that we've kept an emphasis particularly on farm livestock. We have a great horse show as well but the farm livestock is one of the biggest in the United Kingdom and we are delighted

about that because there's no other way that shows a breeder's level of success than competing against another breeder. We have a great saying when we're showing cattle that they're all good ones at home – but when you get them to the show you find out how good they really are.

One of the things the Yorkshire Agricultural Society does is to try to promote and support rural life in general. It obviously has a much wider remit than the Great Yorkshire Show. For example, drystone walling is very much coming back again. A few years ago it was so expensive to actually do the drystone walling that it was declining very fast – walls weren't being maintained. Now there are some monetary government incentives to help and people are becoming more aware that a really good drystone wall is a major asset to a farm. That's just one thing that we are very supportive of, as a society.

We have two different associations of drystone wallers building walls at the show. For one project, we're building a wall round one of our ponds. It's not a case of building it, then knocking it down, it's gradually growing and will stay there for many, many years to come.

Askham Bryan College has one of its satellite campuses here all the year round and both it and Bishop Burton College have stands at the show as well, where they illustrate their own educational programmes.

I think we're doing better now at attracting young people. We were in a difficult time maybe ten years ago but I think the colleges have improved their image in that they're offering a far wider range of courses, not only in agriculture but rural life generally such as conservation programmes, woodland management and so on. There is a greater awareness in farming and the rural community of the need to link back to young people, also in the urban community, who

'In 2006, it was a tremendous honour to be asked to escort the Prince of Wales and the Duchess of Cornwall round the show.'

might like a career in the countryside. I think we're better at talking to them now.

The Society carries out programmes for primary school children around the showground.

We also had a careers day this year where sixth form colleges and schools were invited to come and look at what sort of careers might be available in agriculture and in rural life.

I am more optimistic about the future of farming – as farmers and rural people we're getting better at adapting to the world as it is and not thinking the world should adapt to us and I think that's positive.

In 2006 it was a tremendous honour to be asked to escort the Prince of Wales and the Duchess of Cornwall round the show. It's an honour not many people have and Caroline and I were absolutely delighted to do that but there have been other highlights as well. It's wonderful to have a successful show and a successful exhibit of cattle and sheep and to see our visitors having a good day. It's a lovely feeling to think what the team here has achieved. We're doing something right because people are enjoying it!

The 150th anniversary of the Society was about twenty years ago and this year of course is the 150th show. During both World Wars a number of shows were lost and in 2001, the Foot & Mouth year, the show was

The role of Show Director can involve being placed literally in the firing line! [2006]

cancelled. I don't think, apart from that, a show has ever been lost. Last year we had to put a lot of extra effort into getting the showground fit to use. The weather was a disaster [because of the unprecedented rainfall] but we did it, we had a show and we were quite fortunate with the weather for the event. Some of the car parks were wetter than we would have liked but we put a lot of effort into temporary roadways and we were luckier than some other events in that our show did go ahead.

As for my main interests at the Great Yorkshire, you can't steward all that time in the cattle section without having a great affinity for that part of the show. Our own farm has cattle and sheep so these sections are very high on my list of priorities.

We have an absolutely amazing horse show. Over the last couple of years, we've greatly increased the prize money for the showjumping and I think we now offer the biggest prize money of any of the summer agricultural shows.

It varies with the different classes but the Cock o' the North, which is the showjumping finale and the main class, has total prize money of around £22,000. We have not only the best riders in the world in Yorkshire but also they bring their best horses, which is just as important. It's a great tradition of the show – we have a grandstand which holds over

3,000 people that is full for those showjumping classes and that's wonderful.

There have been some funny incidents over the years but they don't always relate well out of context. Going back to cattle, it's certainly not amusing for the people who are taking part but when the crowd are all sitting round the ring the thing that amuses them most is if any animal breaks away from its handler and goes round the ring. We have all the gates shut so it can't get out. The person who is leading it thinks it's an absolute disaster but everybody else in the world thinks it's such great fun!

We have a superb pig show and we hold the final of a competition called Pig of the Year. If you win any other major show in the United Kingdom, you qualify for the Pig of the Year final, so we get pigs from all over the country. We are very honoured that it's held with us. One of the things that has been most amusing over the years has been the One Man and his Pig competition where lay people try to get pigs to do things that pigs don't particularly want to do, such as move in a certain direction.

Although the Royal Show is being held a couple of days before us, I feel quite comfortable that we will co-exist reasonably well. I think there is a potential for conflict in the livestock areas because some people will choose one show or the other but the feedback that we're getting indicates that we will have excellent, well-filled classes. We know our trade stands are going to be full. When livestock schedules were sent out, the number of requests for schedules was very positive. We are confident but never complacent.

Our prize money is better than most but people don't just show livestock for the money – although it's nice when prize money helps to pay your expenses. Blue Tongue is potentially a problem. We're currently within the Blue Tongue zone but what we don't know is if these zones are going to move before the show. It does present us with a problem but we're doing our best to tackle it. If for some reason a section of the show suffers a restriction, whether it be wet weather, plague or pestilence, we'll give an unequivocal guarantee to refund all money to both livestock and trade stand exhibitors. Some other societies don't do that. I think that's a reassurance to people.

This year we are hoping that livestock exhibits, horse exhibits and trade stand exhibits will be the best for 150 years – time will tell."

Chris Coleman at the Great Yorkshire Show. [2004]

'A VERY GOOD BALANCE'
CHRIS COLEMAN

Honorary Life Vice-President of the Great Yorkshire Show, Chris Coleman farms at Church Farm, Speeton, Filey, which has been in the family since 1921. The 500-acre farm used to be a mixed family farm with cattle and sheep and a few pigs and arable but is now all arable.

I'm semi-retired now. I only work seven days a week now instead of eight! But I'm very lucky, I have a son Tim who has managed the farm now for thirteen years. He has three daughters and the middle daughter is keen on farming, so we'll see.

I'm down to six sheep – they're Leicester Longwool, a rare breed. They've been in the family since 1834. I've done the history and we can trace the flock right back to Robert Bakewell's time [1726-1795] in Leicestershire.

Chris Coleman with Leicester Longwools – a rare breed.
Winner at the Royal Show at York in 1948…

I've been attending the Great Yorkshire since 1948. I've only missed one show and that was in 1949 at Wakefield. I've been to every one after that. The first show after the war was on the Knavesmire at York and it was combined with the Royal Show. The first Yorkshire show 'proper' after the war was at the one at Wakefield in 1949. Then it was at Malton in 1950 and it's been at Harrogate ever since.

My earliest memories of the Great Yorkshire are the one on the Knavesmire which was a four-day show. That was the first big show I went to. My father won the championship with a ram.

I became a sheep steward in 1953. I was a steward for 44 years, but I retired from sheep stewarding when I was 65. I'm 77 now. I've been judging for about twenty years at other shows but I couldn't judge before at the Great Yorkshire because we were exhibiting. It's only in later years I've judged at the Great Yorkshire and I'm judging this year.

There have been changes – at the first show I stewarded at in the early fifties, there were 249 sheep entries and I think last year

…Great Yorkshire Show champion in 1968.
(J. Ashworth)

there would be about 1,500 sheep entries. A lot of those sheep exhibitors, that's their holiday for the year – three or four days at the show.

With being a sheep steward over the years, I've seen very little of the rest of the show. It's only in the last ten years I've been able to have a good look round. I try and concentrate on a different section each year. The showground is so big it takes an awful lot of getting round.

I like to see all the livestock, the main ring events and the vintage machinery stand exhibits. For the last few years I've only been one day to the show but when I was stewarding of course I was there for a week.

The work behind the scenes goes on twelve months of the year. I was on the working party when we built the new sheep sheds. We met every month for about two years.

For the first show after 1950 the sheep were way out west near the Young Farmers' and the Ministry buildings, then we moved right towards the east where Sainsbury's is now. When they bought the seven acres – the whole sheep section – we had to move out across Railway Road and then we planned the new sheep buildings.

The Great Yorkshire has been part of my life ever since 1948. It's been an all-the-year-round job working up to the show up to my retiring from stewarding, then I've tended to take a back seat. I have now retired from the Council and from the working party.

The main thing I enjoyed was being on the sheep committee. We have a series of livestock committees and they do all the donkey work at one meeting, usually in the autumn and plan all the judges, classes, the whole lot, and that committee is made up of people from all aspects of sheep and then the cattle one is from all aspects of cattle and so on – very important.

More females are becoming involved, but not as many as I would like to see. There are very few ladies on the Council and there aren't an awful lot of lady stewards. There ought to be. It goes back to when we first moved to Harrogate in the early Fifties. It was run by ex-army and they tended to be very male dominated. All that has all changed but it hasn't changed the numbers of ladies who are taking posts.

I don't think the show needs to change an awful lot. In the last ten years it's done very well because it's kept a very good balance between agriculture and general interest and I think that's why it's solvent financially. I think the Great Yorkshire's success is not bowing down to popular commercialism. They've tried to persuade the society to do that over the years and of course being financially viable we've never needed to do it.

The show is attracting young people and the Young Farmers' movement round here in our district is very go-ahead and very vibrant and they attract other young people, which is very good."

Long-haired handlers and long-haired sheep! Leicester Longwools ('ewe lamb in wool') at the Great Yorkshire about 1970.

ALL CREATURES GREAT AND SMALL

The Great Yorkshire Show provides a wonderful opportunity to see animals, birds and other creatures of all shapes and sizes. We start this broad overview with one of the largest and gradually descend to the microscopic.

Opposite: A very different and more elegant member of the horse kingdom. Manhattan Sark, winner of the two-year old Hunter section. [1996]

Below: The majestic bulk of a Clydesdale towers above its handler. [2006]

Someone off camera must surely be holding onto the rope! Otherwise models Alicia France, age 16, and Diane Hall, 21, would be no match for the great weight of Brutus the bull if he suddenly turned hostile. The previous week he had been male champion at the Royal Show. [2002]

A toy calf may not have quite the aura of Brutus but is certainly more cuddlesome. It is seen here with Jahzarra McConnell from Glasshoughton. [2007]

Phoebe, an alpaca on its best behaviour, poses obligingly with model Amanda Eyre to make a classic photograph. [2007]

Facing the camera but probably unable to see a thing is the winner in the 'Wool on the Hoof' section. The Wensleydale hog is being shown by Jessie Watkinson from Leyburn. [2006]

53

Rare shot of a goat not trying
to escape from its pen! [2007]

One man and his pig. Withersfield Royal
Catalina, a Large White, with Guy Kiddy
from Bedfordshire. [2004]

A pair of sharp-eyed hounds
with Simon Hart, director of
the Countryside Alliance
Campaign for Hunting. [2003]

A big leap for dogs from the
Cyril the Squirrel terrier racing
team. [2007]

Sydney, a six-year old Bald-Headed Eagle, and falconer Chris O' Donnell. [1999]

A rare bird indeed! The 'Little Red Rooster' is shown to Show Director Bill Cowling (left) by sculptor Steve Blaylock. [2005]

A wise and knowing look from Bomber, a European Eagle Owl on the stand of Falconry UK Ltd. [2004]

Left: The white rabbit that was judged supreme champion and gained a silver cup for Thomas Clayborough, age 16 from Harrogate. [2007]

Below left: A wriggling trio firmly grasped by Simon Whitehead of Pakefield Ferrets. [2004]

Below: Bees always attract great interest at the Show. Here they are being carefully handled by Dudley Gue from Beverley. [1999]

A Colley Green Nymph fly is viewed through a magnifying glass by Barry Grantham of the Salmon & Trout Association. [2005]

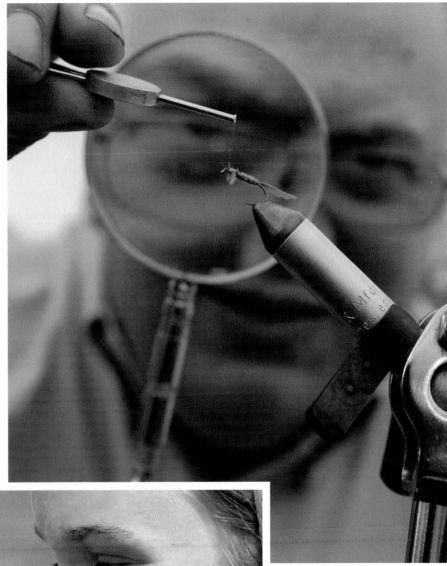

A locust makes eyeball to eyeball contact with Lucy Nelson, age 12, from York. It formed part of a Young Farmers exhibit with the intriguing title 'I'm Not a Farmer Get Me Out Of Here'! [2005]

'THE SHOW IS HEALTHIER THAN EVER' NICK LANE FOX

Chief Ring Steward for the main ring at the Great Yorkshire, Nick Lane Fox lives at Bramham Park, near Wetherby. It has been the family home for the past 300 years and is currently managed by Nick and his wife Rachel. They have five children.

I'm the tenth generation of my family to live at Bramham. It was built by an ancestor in about 1700. I took over from my father in 1997 and I'm doing my best to keep the place going and give it a makeover after 300 years, to make it last for the next 300 years. Although Bramham is very much a family home it is also a thriving business. We're always keen to attract visitors to the 400 acres of historic eighteenth century landscape. The first member of my family who was involved with the Great Yorkshire was the tenth president of the show, George Lane Fox, and five generations since then have been president of the Yorkshire Agricultural Society. The last one was my father, also called George, about twenty years ago.

For my first official role, I started off being a horse steward at the age of twenty-one in 1985. In those days, a new horse steward's first job was stewarding in the donkey classes. Everybody did that. The people showing the donkeys all knew each other. They knew what they were meant to do

Nick Lane Fox, photographed in 2005.

– when to trot up and down and when to stand, so for a steward it was a nice, easy job. They instructed you rather than you instructing them.

I was first taken along to the Great Yorkshire by my mother when I was about six or seven and I think pigs were probably my earliest memory. I remember seeing exhibitors moving pigs around with the board and the stick and I'd never known that they moved pigs like that. Ever since, it's been one of my images – of a Gloucester Old Spot being moved around with the chap in his white coat with his board and his stick.

The other thing you then had to do as a horse steward in the equine breed classes was help the vets to measure the horses or ponies. They all had particular standards for height and a great deal of skulduggery always went on as to whether they could get a bigger horse or pony through the measuring stick. They wanted to be the biggest in their class, not the smallest in the next class up because generally bigger horses and ponies stood out more and therefore caught the eye.

The measuring always happened at seven in the morning. You would get ready with the vets and the vets all knew precisely what they were doing and knew all the scams that everybody could pull. A young steward got every tale such as: 'It was fine last week at such-and-such a show, it got through to the class below there, couldn't you move it to that class for me today?' All that sort of thing went on.

I'm now Chief Ring Steward in the main ring – 2002 was my first year as there was no show in 2001. I've done the main ring since then and that means dealing with everything from making sure that the Dartmoors, the Exmoors, the Dales and the Fells all finish on time, so the ring can be cleared for the next showjumping class, to organising the band at the right moment, all those sort of things. Basically, it means making sure that the ring

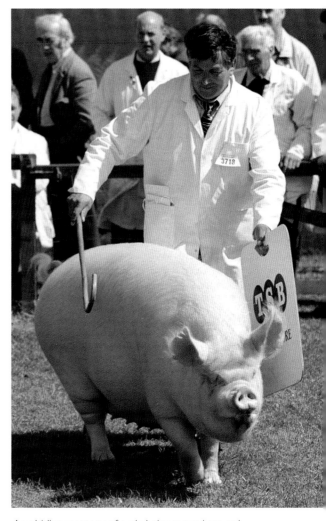

An abiding memory of a pig being moved around with a board and stick and a chap in a white coat – in this case Brian Card from Hampshire. [1996]

runs on time and there's something in there for people to look at for as much of the time as possible. It's always quite fun.

The heavy horses always take longer than you think they're going to. If you try and pack too much in, you suddenly find the ring's running an hour late, which is terrible for competitors who are waiting for their

Contrasting events in the main ring: Four-in-hand coaches parade before the Duke of York. [2002] . . .

classes. They keep coming up and asking when they're going to be on, so that gets a little bit stressful.

We had one moment a few years ago. The White Helmets Motorcycle Display Team, who do all sorts of amazing displays such as getting ten men on a bike and jumping through flaming hoops in formation, needed a particular area which they had marked out with white paint on the arena. The showjumping course builder thought she'd save a bit of time by building some of her fences half into their box. The team refused to go into the ring and start their display until the fences had been moved and the course builder refused to move them. The then president had to come and help the ring stewards and I to move the showjumps. That was quite an interesting day.

I don't really get a great deal of time to get out of the ring. I'm there more or less

from the start of it in the morning until the end. When the showjumping classes are on, the showjumping stewards are very professional and they pretty much run that, and when the cattle parade's on I can usually relax for a little bit then. I always enjoy going round and looking at machinery. I'm a great machinery freak. We have an arable farm at home so I like going and looking at bigger and bigger combines and tractors Yes, it was a boyhood wish – I wanted to be an engine driver, like everybody else!

I always think the Great Yorkshire is a marvellous way to show quite a lot of the urban population of Yorkshire what the rural population of Yorkshire does. If you're standing near the edge of the ring people ask why are you doing this or why are you doing that? I remember once trying to arrange for a class to move to another ring – I think something was running late – and I was

...The Bedale Hunt with their hounds. [2006]

telling the people who were interested in watching the class to occupy the little grandstand next to the control box. But this was not good enough for one lady who asked if we could please move the five of the showjumps, which were ready for the next class, because they were spoiling her view!

That would have taken a good forty-five minutes and twelve men. I had to tell her: 'I'm afraid, madam, we're unable to do that so if you could just stand a little closer to the fence, please.'

The professionalism of the exhibitors has certainly changed a lot. From my view of the main ring one of the main changes has been the rule on chin straps on hats, which has made a visual difference. The ladies' side-saddle class looks a bit different with chin straps and crash hats, rather than top hats and veils, but that's one of the important things one has to do for health and safety nowadays.

I am the only one in my family who is involved in an official capacity at the moment. My brother has in the past been a horse steward but he now lives in Gloucestershire so unfortunately he's unable to take part so much now. But my children are aged sixteen downwards so we'll see if they are interested.

I think the show is healthier than ever. There are more and more horses and cattle in the classes, which is very nice to see. The show is as much of an attraction as it's ever been and I think as most of the population's relationship with farming and the countryside gets more distant, it's more and more important that people see how their food is produced and what happens in the countryside. It's nice to see that there's a vogue for organic food and locally produced produce. Long may that continue.

'ONCE YOU GET THE FARMING COMMUNITY TOGETHER IT'S FANTASTIC' LADY INGILBY

Press Steward at the Great Yorkshire Show, Emma Ingilby graduated from Bristol University with an honours degree in Business Studies. She married Sir Thomas Ingilby of Ripley Castle in 1984 and they have five children. Her husband comments that 'Emma's resourcefulness, vision, determination, energy and total commitment to quality have proved invaluable as we continue to try and make the estate economically viable'.

I'm a Yorkshire lass. I come from York and my mother is from a farming family in Surrey.

My grandfather had an agricultural fertiliser company and used to exhibit at the Great Yorkshire so I just got taken along. My first memory of the show is when I must have been quite young as really I can only remember legs. That's all you can remember isn't it – legs and the kind of animals, which is probably a good memory really.

I'm tall now but I was young then and obviously you had to wear a pretty dress and hair tied up with a ribbon. I love horses - and have always loved horses - so I just desperately wanted to stand next to every horse on the showground.

When you look back the show has got bigger and bigger but I think the content is pretty well the same. I do remember for

Lady Ingilby, photographed at the Great Yorkshire Show in 2006.

example the Army being there when I was in my early teens. Because I was at boarding school we broke up earlier so my father used to say, 'Let's go to the Great Yorkshire Show for the day.' And when I was first courting Thomas he was the president's steward, so I would meet him for lunch and we'd go off after the show for a date and then I'd come back home.

An Ingilby has never been president of the show, possibly because the last few generations have all been career soldiers. My husband went to Cirencester agricultural college, and when we had land he was very active in the show. We've actually sold most of the land to the tenants and have kept just the home farm – it's the way of the world.

I started off at the show just doing odd days helping in the stewards' area, rescuing lots of children and occasionally taking sponsors to lunch. I met Jack Watmough of the Bradford printers, who was press steward for years and was a fantastic man. He knew all about the workings of the press, although of course the press was a different animal then. He then retired and Thomas - my Thomas - was press steward for a while, but it didn't really suit him and it was perhaps a bad time to be one.

Then Giles Worsley, the Duchess of Kent's brother from Hovingham, did the job for a year or two while they looked for someone else. Because I've been in marketing, I was asked to be press steward. I was thrilled to get this role.

I'm still press steward for the moment – definitely for this year – but you always wait for the letter with baited breath to see if you've still got the job. It basically involves looking after the press. We've a full-time PR Manager, who looks after the media's involvement. Once the show is up and running I'm responsible at the end of the day as I'm on Council. If something big went down and I couldn't get hold of anyone else I'm at least empowered to help make a decision.

I love being press steward. I love the press pavilion, even on a bad day when it's all going wrong.

Sometimes there's a funny photograph in the pavilion and we have a 'put a caption on it' competition. We quite often share jokes. There is a belief that you can't say anything in front of the press but in fact you can, and you can have a lot of fun because at the end of the day we all know you have got to trust them. If it's a bad story I can't say 'Don't print it.' It's their job to print it. All I can do is say, 'Give us the right to coment.'

The point about the press is that for every good news story there is always going to be something negative and if it's not the visitor numbers then at the moment it's traffic. It's the natural way but when you're older and wiser you just accept the situation. You can't tell 100,000 people which way to drive even if you try, so at the end of the day we'll answer the criticism – we're trying it the best we can – and that's all we can say. If someone has to queue for three hours we're sorry, but then it is a huge show. The figures tell their own story.

We used to play jokes. It depended who was the president, but we certainly played jokes on some of them. We had a Major General going round in his golf buggy, so while he was at lunch we took his buggy and put roll bars on it, 'go faster' stripes, goggles and a racing helmet. When he came out from lunch his whole vehicle had been completely changed. Another year the president had decided it would be quicker to walk so we had two donkeys delivered.

With Thomas being the president's steward for so long, I don't think we've missed a show apart from the one that was cancelled in Foot & Mouth year in 2001. Even when I was pregnant I managed to get there and work.

I've five children. Our eldest son, Jamie, has worked for the show for quite a few years. He started volunteering because he's very aware of information technology. He used to come and sit, age 13, in the press pavilion, and get onto computers and help, and then he was officially asked three years ago to be a steward. He is following a family tradition. His grandmother stewarded in the overseas pavilion for many years when in her late eighties..

I think the royal visits are always impressive. My daughter Eleanor gave a bouquet to Princess Anne so there are little things like that. She was four. She was so trained: step forward, knee behind, bend, curtsy, give the flowers. You can understand the excitement in any child that gets to give something to a royal.

From my point of view the royals are fantastic because they really do stop and talk to people. They've all been 99 per cent informed about agriculture and shown a genuine interest. They've supported the show very well. The Prince of Wales has been very supportive and has been twice.

Technically the show has moved with the times but I think the content has been quite carefully kept. It is not walking away from agriculture, which is still quite firmly there. The Yorkshire Agricultural Society is a charity. Its funds are used to benefit agriculture and not for commercial gain.

If you were just a commercial venture and you were setting up as a promoter, you would make certain decisions differently. For example, the content in the main ring, how much space you gave to the livestock or whatever, or the amount of charity and agriculture-related tradestands, which are all subsidised. But actually the show just about washes its face. If it's a terrible wet year it's likely to struggle but if it's a brilliant sunny year then we're probably going to do very well.

The bottom line is that it's both agriculture and income and finance that is behind it. Because of prudent investment it can afford to make a decision for all the right reasons and not just commercial ones.

It went through this period of deciding whether to move the showground. That is because the town of Harrogate has expanded. You could argue that if you started the whole thing on a new site you could do ideal planning. The show originally used to move round. This is something the Game Fair still does, actually to its cost, because it has to create a new show every year, even though it has three or four main sites. As the cancellation at Harewood proved last year, it can be horrendously expensive all round.

So having decided to stay – and I was one the boundaries of the decision with Thomas on the Council at the time – the fact is that it has meant the Society can invest in it. It is on the edge of Harrogate, but for three days of the year it's Harrogate's biggest attraction.

There's still development of the showground, including farm shops and some form of accommodation that can be used during show day. So I think there's just continuous looking at the showground. A lot of buildings have been developed by the Society. The showground is not just the Great Yorkshire Show any more and it can't afford to be. There are now two shows, the Great Yorkshire and Countryside Live in autumn. They're both important. It means the showground is used for 365 days in the year.

I spend a lot of time on the showground, walking around and talking to people. One of the overwhelming things that really do not change are the characters at the show. The unique characteristic of the show is the Yorkshireness of it. Although they come from all counties around, once you get the farming community together it's fantastic. They come and they go because families change but it's

'One of the overwhelming things that really does not change are the characters at the show.' This group of Harrogate farmers was watching the Ayrshire cattle being judged but finding it all a little tiring! [2003]

still a case of all pulling together and everyone saying 'Hello! How are you?'

I'm optimistic, despite all the difficulties of farming at the present time, and I think it will endure. The role of the Agricultural Society is to help it endure. If it doesn't endure then we haven't done our job.

'VERY PLEASANT MEMORIES'

BERT VERITY

Now in his 95th year, Bert Verity has been involved with the Great Yorkshire Show for 86 years. He has retired from farming although he still keeps a few sheep for a hobby at a village on the outskirts of Harrogate. He is busy writing a book about Great Showmen.

I first went to the Great Yorkshire Show in 1926 when it used to move around. That year it was held on the Stray in Harrogate. The Royal Show moved around as well and when the Royal Show came to Yorkshire they would amalgamate. There weren't any trees planted on the Stray then, it was a big open space. During the Second World War it was all ploughed and cultivated with wheat.

The road wasn't as wide in those days because there was no tarmacadam, just stone roads and only a few motor cars. My father had just got his first Model T Ford. I went to the show with my mother and father and brothers – I would be thirteen years old. The few cars that were there were parked on the side of the road because most people came by train or walked, or by bicycle or pony and trap.

The livestock would come by train or walk. With it being on the Stray it was very close to the station. When I was a kiddie, we farmed at Masham and I remember driving

sheep to the station there.

At the 1926 show I remember all the livestock and I can remember my mother giving me and my brother a shilling each to go and get some bottles of lemonade but you could only get one because the price of everything on the showground was double anywhere else.

My first show days started at Masham when I was ten years old. I'd bought a little bantam on the way home from school, took it to Nidderdale Show and it won the championship.

I've been in sheep all my life because on the 6th of April 1916, a gentleman walked into my father's house at the farm near Masham where I was born and said to my father: 'Come on, Watson, get a move on, the weather's cold.' It was the morning we were moving from one farm to another. That morning we went in the pony and trap after all our things had been moved. The only means of moving livestock was to walk and the only transport was by horse and cart. I was only three years old and it started to snow and by the time we got to the farm everything was white.

A relation of my father, Peter Verity, had had this 750-acre farm and he hadn't any sons so my father took the farm and he also took

Bert Verity, who attended his first Great Yorkshire Show in 1926. [2005]

over his flock of 365 Swaledale ewes and they were all due to lamb that week. When I got into that kitchen, there were about a dozen lambs in front of the big fire. Six inches of snow came that day and it stayed for a fortnight. That was what got me into the sheep because I played with these lambs.

Those were the early days of pedigrees. My father had a flock of pure-bred Wensleydales but there hadn't been any pedigrees until the last years of the nineteenth century. The Shorthorn cattle were the first to be pedigree and then they got on to the various breeds of sheep and Angus cattle and so on.

In the early part of the last century, Britain became the top breeding centre of the world. Our Angus and Hereford bulls went to the Argentine and all over the world. It wasn't until after the last war that we started bringing in continentals.

I became a member of the Yorkshire Agricultural Society in the 1930s. I moved here to Barrowby Grange Farm in 1950. The first year it was at the present Harrogate site was the following year and I've been every show day since. I can remember one day we were very busy haymaking so I couldn't stay all day but I've never missed.

Three of the main men on the committee then were Frank Abbey, Frank Chapman and Leslie Cayly, known as the 'three wise men' – I knew them all and they were the ones who purchased the present site. It wasn't exactly as it is today – there was the obsolete Starbeck railway line running through it. I asked them what made them choose the site because it wasn't ideal when we saw it. They agreed it wasn't, but it was the position. Harrogate was a boom town.

Those same three wise men, who were involved with the initial purchase, also fought to retain it in later years when it was suggested that the site should move. They

Bert Verity at Masham Show in 1946. There could hardly be a greater contrast with today's Great Yorkshire.

had the farming community behind them. I proposed very strongly that we stayed put. You have Harrogate with all the accommodation and entertainment. Harvey Smith told me that he'd been all over the world and there isn't another ring as good as the Great Yorkshire Show.

When the show first came to Harrogate it wasn't the stock that was the main feature, it was the machinery. All the area that is now housing was covered by machinery.

Over the years I've been exhibiting commercial cattle. In 1967 we had Foot and Mouth and we also had TB and there was a shortage of dairy cattle. The big cow byres were half empty. They didn't used to accept any livestock at the Great Yorkshire unless it

was pedigree. Commercials, of course, are not pedigree. Frank Abbey used to show his Friesian cattle at all the shows, and I used to show commercial cattle. Frank, who was chief cattle steward for many years, agreed the Great Yorkshire would have to accept commercial cattle but asked me if I thought they would come. I told him if they gave prize money, they would come.

So the commercial cattle were first exhibited in 1970 and it was a great success. On the showground they had offices dotted along the cattle lines for different breeds. There were a lot more dairy cattle originally than there was beef cattle. The Guernseys more or less disappeared leaving spare stalls so, after two years, I asked Frank Abbey if I

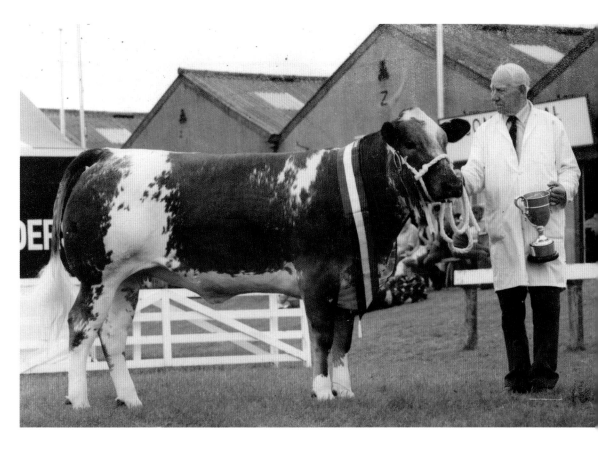

Overall commercial beef champion at the Great Yorkshire in 1983.

could have the Guernsey stall to convert. My wife made some curtains, and I painted it out, made a bar, put in seats and I've had it ever since. I had a signpost made: 'Commercial beef'.

I have never sought any official involvement at the Great Yorkshire. I used to show at all the other shows and a lot of the small ones thought the Great Yorkshire was too officious – all rules and regulations when it was in the early days.

It's changed over the years. When I first went it was only small showground. It had been a stone quarry where the sheep are now. Harrogate was built out of stone from there and then they closed the quarry, filled it in and it was a car park for many years.

Knowing so many show people, I said to my friend Joe Stoney who is the show director of Nidderdale Show and was awarded the MBE last year, 'Let's organise a Showmen's Club, there's a show in the summer but nothing in the winter.' He thought it was a good idea so that was started up about twelve years ago and it's a great success. In the first December we had two hundred people for a dinner at Millstone's, on the Skipton Road out of Harrogate, and it was full to capacity. We've eighteen shows in our club at the moment. Each year on the first Friday in December we invite one of the shows to come and act as host to our dinners and this Christmas, 2008, it will be the turn of the Great Yorkshire.

Bert Verity with some of his Texels. (photo: Farmers Guardian)

I asked Christopher Hall if it was it possible for the Showmen's Club to get a stand and a marquee on the showground near the livestock. Bill Cowling got us a lovely site just above the pigs. It's been there ever since and it's turned out to be an excellent get-together at the Great Yorkshire.

For the last two years I've never even seen the main ring. I go a week before to get the marquee and the offices ready and put the curtains up. I have people who run it for me now, a barman and so on, and it runs like a clock because they do it every year. I've got a good caterer. We have breakfast from seven in the morning, a buffet lunch, then we have an evening meal at half past five.

My friends come from all over and after breakfast on the first day I go down and see the sheep judging. I exhibited Texel sheep and so does my son Michael. Then I come back to my marquee and at half past twelve they judge the commercial cattle. By the time

we've had our evening meal the traffic's gone. The next day I spend all day in the marquee because I have so many people coming in.

It was my idea to promote an autumn/winter show, which developed into Countryside Live. I got it started but after the first couple of years, at my age I didn't want to be involved with a new show in an official capacity.

We exhibited sheep and cattle for over forty years at local and national shows, including Smithfield, except in 1976 when I had the honour to judge it. I've also judged at many other shows all over the British Isles. My father Watson Verity was recognised to be a top judge of both cattle and sheep and so was my uncle, William Verity. They were very keen showmen. My great-grandfather was recorded as winning the overall championship with his Wensleydale tup and Swaledale ewe at Masham show in 1803.

Over the years at shows I've met many members of the royal family several times. I was introduced to Princess Anne at one show. The steward was explaining that the championship had just been awarded to a cross bred. She seemed to be at a loss as to why pedigrees had been beaten by a crossbred. I just said to her: 'It's like this, my dear – they're like you, they've got a foreign dad and an English mum.'

I have a lot of experience of the Great Yorkshire in the past but I don't look back on anything in my life. I shall be ninety-five in August but I still look forward. When I think of the show, I'm visualising what it will be like in another twenty years' time. I am optimistic about its future, although farming is going through the most depressed time. I've seen many governments and I had the privilege of meeting Winston Churchill when I served on the War Agricultural Committee during the war. In 1941, just after the Battle of Britain, I was summoned one morning with other colleagues to meet at Darlington.

The door opened and who should walk in but Winston himself. I can remember every word he said: 'Our brave airmen have won the Battle of Britain. Hitler thought he could bomb us into submission but thanks to our brave airmen we defeated them. Now he thinks he can starve us into submission. I'm here this morning to appeal to you gentlemen to go out into the countryside and appeal to every farmer and every person that has a garden to grow a bit more. You farmers have always been treated by this government as a very special case – and always will be because you are the creators of this green and pleasant land that our soldiers, sailors and airmen are all fighting for. I am appealing to you to whatever you can. I know you will do your best.'

I think one of the secrets of the Great Yorkshire's success is that it owns its own showground and is responsible for the management of it. My hope is to see it continue for years and years to come because sadly we are losing our markets. Pannal closed in 1994. Wetherby ceased because it's all arable round there now, along with Boroughbridge, Ripon, Bridgend, Otley and now Masham. That has left a vacuum in the agricultural world.

We have got to support the Great Yorkshire. I've seen Countryside Live start, I've seen the Showmen's Club start but I would like to see a few other things held through the year to support the farming community in this area. I would like to see a few more farmers' get-togethers and farmers' markets – my granddaughter has one in Harrogate. I would like to see more use made of the existing buildings. The sheep sheds are second to none. They could be used for many exhibitions, demonstrations, breed society shows and so on. Likewise, all the vast numbers of cattle sheds. The British public need to know more about food production

Shakespeare, one of the family's finest Texel tups, which won first prize in 1989.

and British agriculture. Get the breed societies working, the National Farmers' Union and the Country Landowners' Association. I would like to see the show diversify throughout the year. It is such a fantastic site.

My memories of the Great Yorkshire Show over the years have been very pleasant ones. It's been something to look forward to and, because I'm adjacent to it, I still treat it as my local show. It is a local show now to many people because some of the smaller shows are struggling to keep going.

I like to go there to meet people and now people know where I am so they come and find me in the hospitality marquee. A number of the committee come and join in. It gives people chance to relax. We will be celebrating the 150th show in the Showmen's Marquee this year, with various new attractions.

As long as I'm able to, I shall support the Great Yorkshire Show and give them any advice I can.

ACTION!

Activity takes many forms at the Great Yorkshire Show. Here's just a small selection of the numerous possibilities.

BALANCING: 'Flying Gunners', the Royal Artillery motorcycle display team, thrill the crowd with a pyramid. [2005]

CARVING: Dominic Suddaby makes a shepherds' crook. One careless slip of the knife can spell disaster. [2004]

CELEBRATING: Emma Thomas and fiancé Nigel Curran toast their impending nuptials at the place where it all began three years earlier. [2007]

CLIMBING: Hollyoaks TV star 'Sally Hunter' (Katherine Blyton from York) is coping well with the popular pole climb. [2005]

COOLING DOWN: An ice cream is much appreciated by Norman Sutcliffe, age 75, from Todmorden on a hot July day. [2007]

CONCENTRATING: 81-year old Hugh Evans of the Salmon & Trout Association gives fly-fishing tuition with a vintage 1950s Milwards Flymaster split cane rod. [2004]

JUMPING: Flying through the air with the greatest of ease – or so it appears during the Newton Badsworth Stakes. [2006]

LIFTING: A dramatic shot of James Marshall carrying straw bails. They were needed for a fashion show by students from Leeds University's School of Design.

PLAYING: Constructive activity for the very young in the Education Area is much appreciated by parents. [2004]

RUNNING: Young girl clearly in a hurry as she clutches her bouquet. [2006]

SHELTERING: Umbrellas unfurled to watch the cattle parade in the main ring. [2004]

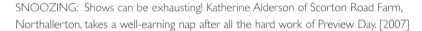

SNOOZING: Shows can be exhausting! Katherine Alderson of Scorton Road Farm, Northallerton, takes a well-earning nap after all the hard work of Preview Day. [2007]

WASHING: A Hereford heifer receives a good hosing down from Phil Allman. [2007]

TASTING: The Prince of
Wales enjoys a light bite.
[2006]

WINNING: The 'Supreme Champion' NFU stand – and Graham Wood,
chairman of its Horticulture Board. [2007]

'I WOULD MISS THE GREAT YORKSHIRE HUGELY'

MARGARET CHAPMAN

Chief Cattle Steward at the Great Yorkshire Show, Margaret Chapman has arable farmland and grassland at Bishopthorpe, York. For six months in the summer, she has a facility for touring caravans.

My father showed at the Great Yorkshire and his father and grandfather before him. My great-grandfather, Joseph Andrew Chapman, was showing Dairy Shorthorn at the Great Yorkshire in 1910, so that's nearly 100 years of family involvement.

In 1927 when he was thirteen, my father won the junior section of the first ever Young Judges' Competition at the Great Yorkshire held in Darlington.

The first show I remember participating in was in 1944 at the Red Cross Agricultural Show held in York – it was a family affair, we were all showing cattle. I showed a British Friesian calf 'Herrington Ketchup', winning my first rosette. In 1948 when the Royal Show was held on the Knavesmire at York, we attended as a family but did not show cattle. In 1950 I remember visiting the Great Yorkshire Show held at Malton, helping with the preparation of the animals to be shown. I don't remember seeing much of the rest of the show. We were always involved with cattle and I think I had the impression in those days that shows only had cattle!

A recent photograph of Margaret Chapman at the Great Yorkshire Show.

The whole concept of the Great Yorkshire has always interested me and I have enjoyed watching it grow. The interest in food and how it is produced and what food contains is so important these days, the Food Hall has evolved and grown into a large section of the Show. I still don't have much time to look at the rest of the show because the three days are very busy in the cattle area. I may have a little bit of time on a Thursday. The Grand Cattle parade held on both the second and third days of the show in the main ring is an important event for both the exhibitors and the public. The superb commentary by Christine Moore informing the viewers about the various breeds and the prize winners makes it an interesting hour's entertainment. I just love the whole of the show and what it does for agriculture and hopefully to bring town and country closer together.

I first started as a cattle steward – and I'm not sure if I wasn't the first lady cattle steward – in 1975 and then I became a senior steward in 1985. I was one of the first two ladies to be invited to what was previously an all-male pre-show dinner. Myself and the late Marjorie Hodgson who was involved with education were the first two ladies to be invited. Nowadays, there are a lot of ladies invited, but it was quite an honour in 1985!

Everybody who helps, I know certainly in the cattle section, just love to be involved and want it to be a success. It's a great team of people who help, they really are wonderful. We have twenty breeds of pedigree cattle plus the commercials so we have twenty-one sections in the cattle section alone. All have to be judged so they all need a ring steward and an assistant steward at least. So you're talking about forty to forty-five stewards helping in the cattle section alone.

We're getting increasing pressures these days from Health and Safety and rules have to be abided by. We didn't have anything like that in 1975 – of course we were always

Margaret Chapman in 1944, age five-and-a-half, confidently leading 'Herrington Ketchup' at the Red Cross Agricultural Show in York.

careful but we have definite guidelines to go by now and all the risk assessments have to be carried out. We have schoolchildren who carry boards for various events such as the Grand Cattle Parade advertising each of the beef and dairy breeds. Risk assessments have to be carried out to assess the possible hazards likely to affect the health and safety of the persons concerned – such as an animal getting loose or the child stepping in animal waste or even the weather has to be taken into account.

The general public too have come under certain restrictions when moving in the livestock area. Whereas people used to be very free to walk about the sheds, now, when the cattle are moving in and out of the show rings as they are being shown, the sheds now have to be cordoned off. This is a shame for the public but people are just not aware of what animals and livestock can do in certain circumstances.

My father had the herd of Bishopthorpe pedigree British Friesians. He sold up a long time ago and became involved with pedigree livestock exports. I worked with him exporting pedigree livestock all over the world, up until BSE stopped all livestock exports from this country.

It was an interesting era, meeting people from all over the world. I visited many places including Iran several times in the Shah's day in the late 1960s, also Saudi Arabia, Canada and America many times. Livestock exports were very buoyant in the seventies and I was in charge of the exports to Canada, USA and New Zealand as well as participating with overseas visitors who came over to select their own pedigree animals. We had buyers from many parts of the world including Japan, Russia, Libya, Africa, South America, Kuwait, Algeria, Hungary, China, Thailand and – closer to home – Holland, Germany, France, Portugal and Spain. I was pleased I was involved at such an interesting time of the livestock era.

Nowadays, some pedigree livestock are exported, but with embryo transfer and semen available for export, there is not the need for the transit of live animals at a huge cost.

At the show, we've seen different breeds become more buoyant. The Limousins were always small in numbers, but now they're one of the master breeds. We usually have good classes of Limousins and Charolais. We still have a very good attendance of the ten native beef breeds, which is very encouraging. It's wonderful to see the Belted Galloways, Highlanders and Dexters, Longhorns and the like. On Wednesday of the show we have a Native Breed Championship where all ten Native Breed Champions compete for the Overall Native Championship – a good competition to watch.

The dairy cattle have gone down in numbers. We used to get a huge amount of dairy cattle. In the old days, people would go to the Royal Show and then they would come up to the Great Yorkshire and then they'd go down to the East Midland at Peterborough. That has died out now, partly because of cost and keeping herdsman and cattle away from the farm, but having said that, we still get a good attendance of dairy cattle.

Standards have improved over the years. It's interesting to look at old photographs of the old breeds; they were stumpy but now they've got taller and stronger, better boned. Conformation wise, they're much better. They have changed, especially in the dairy section. When we were showing cattle it was the dual-purpose black and white animal. Now the black and white Holstein animal is purely for dairy; it is a much finer boned, a much larger animal that produces more milk than the smaller British Friesian did.

At the Great Yorkshire Show we do try to encourage younger people. We have classes on the Wednesday for the Dairy Young Handlers competition. They show maiden heifers and we have the three age groups of youngsters. It gets more and more popular every year and this year we're starting for the first time in the beef section with two age groups and seeing how that goes. There are a

The cattle section at the Great Yorkshire remains buoyant. The overall enthusiasm is reflected in this photograph of Robert Benson, the Yorkshire Post Agricultural Correspondent, with the winning Simmental team in the Interbreed Beef Championship. [2003]

lot of young people who are interested and so capable, which is good for the future of showing livestock

Difficulties occur in the livestock section with the entries. Last year we had to limit the number of animals any one exhibitor could enter as we have only a limited number of stalls available; but we also have to allow for cancellations. We had a number of people on the waiting list, wanting to show their animals. There has to be a cut-off period then they go on a waiting list. As soon as anybody drops out prior to the show, they get their stalling fees back so it pays them to advise the office and then we can invite the next one on the waiting list. Even though the animals haven't been accepted officially, they will have been catalogued.

I am optimistic about the industry. I think the success of the Great Yorkshire is due to its good management over many years. Now we

have a highly respected Show Director, Bill Cowling, who is a great leader and farmer, and a great team working in the Society's offices who all have one aim – for the Great Yorkshire Show to be a success.

I would miss the Great Yorkshire hugely if I was no longer involved. I was in a car accident recently in South America and the first thing that I recall when I came round was saying: 'I haven't told anyone I want the Jerseys to lead the parade this year.'

That honestly is the first recollection I had. The Jerseys have always come into the Grand Parade last but I have introduced a new competition for the 150th show and it will take place during the Grand Parade. I decided the Jerseys should lead the Grand Parade in. I had discussed everything about the new competition with the office but I hadn't mentioned that bit, so hopefully that will happen.

'THE COMPETITION IS ALWAYS HOT' DAVID BROOME

Born in Cardiff in 1940, David Broome is a retired showjumping champion. He three times won the European championships in the 1960s and individual Olympic bronze medals in 1960 and 1968, and in 1970 the world championship. He won the King George V Gold Cup on six different horses between 1960 and 1991 – a record yet to be equalled.

I went to the Great Yorkshire Show most years from the mid-1960s to the early 1990s. I was always very lucky and several times won the famous Cock o' the North Championship on the final day. What a wonderful name for a championship – and so very northern!

I took my best-known horse, Mister Softee, three or four times. He was a great draw as it was on him that I gained a bronze medal at the Mexico Olympics in 1968 and was only two fences behind the gold medal position. The unique Great Yorkshire Show arena seems to be a good training ground for potential Olympic horses and riders, as so many have competed here down the years.

Mister Softee was owned by John Massarella of Doncaster and won pretty much everything that was anything in the mid 1960s. He was previously ridden by my friend John Lanni. His son Matthew won the

David Broome, whose presence in the showjumping ring at the Great Yorkshire was an eagerly anticipated event for almost thirty years.

Cock o' the North on Ultra.

I made some very good friends at the Great Yorkshire. I watched the Whitakers – all Yorkshire born and bred! – grow up and become the leading showjumping family. Graham Fletcher was always a great mate and I married his sister.

I also became a close friend – and rival –

of Harvey Smith. He once beat me into second place in the 'Cock' after I had won it the previous year. Harvey was always rather unlucky at the show, but I have many special memories. One year there were too many entries, but Harvey remained forceful and refused to be defeated. It was arranged that one competitor had to go over the starting line as another crossed the finishing line. In that way we got through sixty competitors in an hour. It was amazing!

I'm a Welshman and so always got on well with Major Reg Whitehead from Monmouthshire. He was responsible for constructing the courses. It was enormous with some really big and high jumps and was miles in front of other courses. There was often a double wall five feet six inches high going in and a very solid six-feet high wall coming out. There was also a triple bar called 'Follifoot', after a nearby village, which was certainly not for the faint-hearted.

The competition is always very hot at the Great Yorkshire. If you can survive there you can survive anywhere. You feel that it is Yorkshire against the rest and I represented some of the rest!

It is all superbly done and very well organised. It is clear that Yorkshire people are immensely proud of their own show. It is a fashion turn-out and the show is given the respect it deserves. The prize money is now superb and the whole event has been lifted to new heights with more than two thousand horses and ponies now competing.

Going to the Great Yorkshire Show helped to build up a kaleidoscope of knowledge and experience. It all came in handy when I set up the Wales and the West show-jumping and dressage centre at Mount Ballon Manor, near Chepstow. This is run by the Broome family. I'm delighted that my other son Matthew has recently competed at the Great Yorkshire and took second place in the Cock o' the North Championship.

The Cock o' the North Championship in more recent times, with Robert Smith riding Senator Caloubet Du Rouhet. [2007]

'THE ONLY SHOW I WOULD ALWAYS GO TO'

TRICIA JOHNSON

Equestrian journalist Tricia Johnson looks back on twenty years of covering a show that has a unique standing among horse breeders, owners and riders. It is an event that has managed to retain its own identity in changing times, and she always anticipates it with pleasure.

One of Britain's most treasured rural traditions is that of the county show, and none is more highly regarded in equestrian circles than the Great Yorkshire.

My first visit to Harrogate on behalf of Horse and Hound (generally regarded as the 'bible' of the horse world) was in 1988, when I was still rather a 'rookie' equestrian reporter. The prospect of covering the showing and show jumping classes was extremely daunting but that first visit, far from proving the nightmare I had feared, got me hooked and I have not missed one single Great Yorkshire Show since then.

Even a bout of pneumonia in 1996 failed to stop me. I had become ill while covering the Royal Show (one of my least favourite assignments!) and had been confined to bed with an undiagnosed high fever for more than a week. When a new doctor finally discovered what was indeed wrong, just four days before the Great Yorkshire began, he put me on antibiotics and ordered me to stay in

Tricia Johnson at home in Spain with her Andalucian stallion Temperano.

bed for at least a week. My immediate retort was: 'Don't be silly, I'm at the Great Yorkshire on Tuesday!' His reply: 'I don't think so, my dear, you'll be far too weak.'

Needless to say, I disobeyed orders and drove up to Harrogate on the Tuesday morning. He was right about one thing, though – I certainly was weak and could walk no further than a dozen yards before what energy I had gave out. This was when friends, colleagues, show officials and exhibitors rallied round, finding chairs for me everywhere I went, running after competitors whom I needed to interview and bringing them to me. Everyone rallied round and generally made things as easy as they possibly could.

In retrospect, I was terminally stupid to have insisted on covering the show, and it took me a long time to recover fully, but I wouldn't have missed it for the world.

I will also never forget the kindness of my landlady, Doreen Nelson, with whom I always stay. She runs a small bed and breakfast house in Hampsthwaite and I regard her as an 'honorary auntie.' Nothing is ever too much trouble but that year she was my saviour – looking after me as if I were family.

I was again on duty when the young and then up-and-coming hunter producer, county-born Robert Walker, achieved his first-ever Great Yorkshire win. He had won at the Horse of the Year Show the previous year, and was fresh from a notable victory at the Royal, but this was the pinnacle as far as he was concerned. And I will never forget his quote: 'Horse of the Year was great, but to win here is just magic: better than getting the chance to go to bed with Caprice!'

I endeavoured to look suitably impressed, but had no idea who Caprice was. When someone else enlightened me later – she was a 'Page Three' model – it did put the quote into perspective, although I had to tone

it down a bit for Horse and Hound!

Another year, the press officer, Judy Thompson, suggested me for a 'live to camera' piece for BBC Look North, who wanted someone to talk about the show jumping classes at the show.

I had done quite a few radio broadcasts, both live and recorded, but this was completely new territory and, frankly, I was terrified. It was due to be done on the final day, as an introduction to the Cock o' the North class, and I spent the whole show becoming more and more worried – almost to the extent where I could think of nothing else.

In the event, the scheduling was changed at the eleventh hour and I was not needed – I almost cried with relief.

Show jumping at the Great Yorkshire has a following unique in the whole country. Not only does it draw unprecedented numbers of knowledgeable spectators to the ringside, but top international riders regard winning the Cock o' the North as a massive 'plus' on their CV and the July dates get pencilled into their often-crowded schedules before any others. It is not uncommon for all four of Britain's Olympic team members to be at Harrogate, and Harvey Smith's son, Robert, and the Whitaker brothers, for instance, have often 'commuted' back and forth from a show in Europe in order to compete.

The ringside and stands were packed to overflowing in 1995 when John Whitaker's legendary grey, Milton, made his farewell appearance, galloping round the great arena to the strains of the partnership's theme tune, Tina Turner's 'Simply the Best', with the spectators singing along. As John raised his hat to acknowledge the deafening applause, there was barely a dry eye in the house.

Even this most stoical of Yorkshiremen had need of a handkerchief as he rode Milton out of his 'home' arena for the very last time.

John and Milton, winners of the 'Cock' in 1991, had a Europe-wide fan club to rival any

Robert Smith riding Ublesco in the Cock o' the North Championship before being presented with the coveted trophy by David Forrest. [2005]

pop star, and a few months previously the pair had made a similar appearance at Gothenburg horse show as part of Milton's farewell tour. Tina Turner had been performing in the city and the show organisers had managed to persuade her to make a surprise appearance and sing her song live.

As John recounted this story to me, saying what a magical moment it had been, he cleared his throat and added quietly: 'But it was nothing compared to the reception we got in there today. I couldn't believe it.'

For many years the show was renowned for its highly individual show jumps. Every year George Thackray's trademark 'Liverpools' and others would emerge, freshly painted, to give the arena that special 'Yorkshire' feel.

This did cause problems, though, as even seasoned international horses would sometimes need a second -- or third -- look before jumping these 'strange' obstacles. But their riders – a breed not normally renowned for keeping any complaints under wraps – would just shrug their shoulders, hoping that their horses would perform better the following day, as indeed they usually did.

Eventually the sport's governing bodies insisted on lighter, more modern obstacles – the old jumps were incredibly heavy – and now, only the famous double of walls remains from those days. It is used solely in the Cock o' the North.

The camaraderie in the press room is also something special and, compared to several other shows, the Great Yorkshire is the one event which the press anticipate with pleasure, rather than 'just another piece of work.'

The greatest compliment I can pay to the Great Yorkshire is that it is the only show I would always go to, without fail, even if I was not working.

DRESSED FOR THE DAY

Like virtually everything else at the Great Yorkshire Show, modes of dress are noted for their huge variety. The next few pages range from the elegant to the extraordinary.

Fashions change, sometimes for the worse but often for the better. There is something rather splendid about the formal elegance of the two stewards admiring a tractor in 2007. It contrasts with the more casual wear of the three stewards posing for the camera in 1956.

There is nothing self-conscious about styles of dress at the show, as it is considered far more important to concentrate on the many events on offer. Formal and informal attire here rub shoulders, but the group as a whole is engrossed in the judging in the cattle ring. [2006]

The fashion shows at the Great Yorkshire have a keen following. Model Josephine Kime is wearing a vintage style cape in grey tweed with burnt edge and beading detail designed by Carla Gawron from Wakefield. She was preparing for an event hosted by the Textile Centre of Excellence in Huddersfield. [2006]

The impressive uniforms of the King's Troop can hardly fail to be noticed. [2004]

All black! The Bishop of Knaresborough, James Bell, and Linburn Echo of Low Hall Farm, Dacre. The Aberdeen Angus won first prize in the AA Bull Class. [2004]

White coats to the fore as judge David Thomlinson weighs up the Yorkshire Post Interbreed Team. [2007]

'Hunting pink' on horseback as the Devon & Somerset Staghounds eagerly await the 'off'. [1999]

A Scottish touch is brought by Ken Pickles from Addingham. The strident tones of the bagpipes seem to be upsetting Betris Gael of Coverhead Farms, winner of the Highland heifer class. Keeping her under control is farm manager David Maughan. [2007]

Formal dress and white tie is de rigueur for Casablanca Steps as they provide some sophisticated music. [2007]

99

Return of the Romans! George Haritakis (Pavius) and Keith Mulhern (Maximus Gluteous) mingle with the crowds as they promote the York Roman Festival. [2007]

Bill and Ben (alias Aimée Barham, age 17, from Leeds, and Kim Wilson, also 17, from Harrogate) promote safety in the garden. [2002]

A woodpecker keeps abreast of the news! Jane Hamilton, age 16, was acting as the Yorkshire Agricultural Society's education mascot. [2004]

'ONE OF THE FOREMOST SHEARING VENUES'

BOB RICHARDSON

Chief Sheep Shearing Steward at the Great Yorkshire Show, Bob Richardson has farmed near Beverley for forty years since he and his wife moved into their farmhouse that dates back to the early 1700s. They have a pedigree flock of Oxford Down sheep and Shorthorn cattle. Bob was a lecturer at Bishop Burton College and is an assessor for NPTC (National Proficiency Test Council). He and Jean have a son and daughter and two grandchildren.

I only came up to Yorkshire for a year from Warwickshire but I met Jean at Young Farmers and I'm still here… that was in 1966.

Our Oxford Down flock is one of the oldest in the flock book – it was founded by my grandfather in 1898. I used to show Shorthorn cattle with my uncle, Joe Hutchinson, who was a regular at the Great Yorkshire for many years.

I was first taught to shear at the Warwickshire Agricultural College. It takes some years of practice to perfect the art and you must be physically fit to handle the sheep. My top tip for a learner would be to attend a British Wool Marketing Board training course and then work with an experienced shearer.

At one time, shearing was a communal effort for local farms, the men getting together to wash sheep in a pond or river and then shear them by hand. Nowadays it's done by machine, which is much quicker, of course. It was when electricity got round to farms in the 1940s and '50s that shearing machines became the norm. Godfrey Bowen came from New Zealand and revolutionised the technique by introducing his own method that we still use today. Godfrey has visited Harrogate on two occasions with the New Zealand team. The best shearers can turn out sheep in under a minute whereas blade shearing can take four to five minutes.

On-farm shearing begins in May and continues into July. Professionals will be shearing up to 300 sheep a day and many travel to New Zealand for their season, which is our winter.

My involvement with the Great Yorkshire began about ten years ago as an assistant sheep steward. Then five years ago I was asked to be the Chief Steward for the shearing section on the retirement of Jon Vicary who had built it up over many years.

Shearing first began at Harrogate with demonstrations on a farm trailer, progressing to a more permanent four-stand arrangement and then, in 1995, the present six-stand stadium, which is one of the finest in the country.

Bob Richardson with one of his Oxford Down sheep. [2000]

Each year we try to make improvements – this year, for instance, we're introducing a competition for the Champion Shearer of Yorkshire. We usually have up to 130 competitors from all over the UK and abroad, including the New Zealand team. One year we had a team from the Falkland Islands.

There are over thirty shearing competitions run under the rules of the British Isles Shearing Competition Association (BISCA), which as been in existence for 29 years. I represent the Great Yorkshire at the BISCA and English Shearing Committee annual meetings.

We use the Swaledale, which is our native Yorkshire sheep breed, and over 1,500

are needed for the three days of the show – training on the Tuesday, competitions on the Wednesday and demonstrations on the Thursday. Sheep are sourced from local farmers who are able to provide the quality required and we very much appreciate their co-operation.

The competitions consist of five classes – Junior, Intermediate, Senior, Open and Blade. Shearers progress up the classes as they become more proficient and achieve success in the competitions and will finally be up against some of the best shearers in the world when they reach Open standard.

Each year, we invite twelve judges. They travel from all over the British Isles to judge

Winners of the 2007
competitions.
Opposite: Trevor
Dobson, the Senior
winner.
Right: Dave Harker,
Junior winner, with (left)
Bob Richardson and
Charles Brook of the
Worshipful Company of
Woolmen.
(courtesy British Wool
Marketing Board)

the shearers as they compete and also the finished sheep. The scores are fed into a computer to produce the final results. Competitors are judged on speed and efficiency and well turned out sheep. This all attracts large crowds who watch the action, listen to the commentary and watch the scoring as it's digitally displayed over each shearer.

The excitement mounts as the finals approach. A presentation ceremony is held at the end of the day's competitions. The Society has increased the Open Prize money to celebrate the show's 150th anniversary. We're fortunate to have very generous commercial sponsors and we are also grateful to the Worshipful Company of Woolmen for giving training bursaries.

Competitors travel great distances, so we try to make them welcome and provide a hospitality unit for refreshments, changing, preparing equipment and relaxing. Judges comment on the excellent hospitality at the Great Yorkshire and we try to ensure that everyone has an enjoyable day with us.

The successful running of a shearing competition depends on teamwork and I was fortunate to inherit a keen and helpful

committee (Eddie Hollins, Richard Caton, Roger Charney, Phil Hargreaves, Richard Walker, Mark Ewbank, Paul Ewbank, Gary Cook, Jim Caygill and Henry Watson). As well as our official autumn meeting and our get-together a couple of months before the show, we keep in touch throughout the year.

On the day there are nearly thirty of us helping – the sheep transporters, handlers round the back of the stand sorting sheep and holding sheep for the pen judges, lads and young ladies (who are shearers themselves) rolling and packing the shorn wool on the front of the stand under the watchful eye of the chief wool packer. Then we also have administration staff, timekeepers, computer operatives and commentators. At the end of the day, the wool goes off to the grading depots and the shorn sheep are returned to their owners.

We are well supported by the Show Director and permanent staff and although UK sheep numbers are in decline and disease restrictions are always a cause for concern, I am confident that the Great Yorkshire will continue to be one of the foremost shearing venues in the country.

'A SOURCE OF TRUSTED INFORMATION'

JAYNE HICKINBOTHAM

Chief Steward for the Cheese & Dairy show at the Great Yorkshire, Jayne Hickinbotham is a self-employed dairy product technologist and is based at Dee Dairy Services in Wrexham, North Wales.

The Cheese & Dairy show was reintroduced in 2002 and I was involved in the inception, the proposals, the planning and the operational side of running it. The other organisational partners, in addition to the show office, are Wensleydale Dairy Products and we work very closely together on the layout of the show, the schedule of judging and the results and the presentation and public information that follows the competition. Morrisons are great – they write out the cheque to make it all happen.

Some older people in the dairy industry remember they used to have a Cheese & Dairy show at the Great Yorkshire but it lapsed around the late Fifties, early Sixties. After the Foot & Mouth low morale in 2001, the Yorkshire Show felt that, to boost the industry and the show, they would put more impetus into representing dairy industries and products from it so they approached Wensleydale Dairy Products about setting up a dairy show. Wensleydale Dairy Products then contacted me knowing that I had already done some organisational work at other agricultural cheese competitions and we put together a proposal that the Yorkshire Agricultural Society liked very much and off it went.

All the judging takes place on Monday afternoon and on the Tuesday morning at 11.15 the Cheese & Dairy show opens to the public and exhibitors. By the time they walk in, the area will have been decorated, the rosettes, the prize cards, public information displayed and everything made ready for the big presentation and top prizes to be awarded to the winning dairies and cheese makers.

There are classes for all dairy products including ice cream, butter, cream, yoghurt, and all types of cheese. We get entries from the big companies in the UK, Europe and even New Zealand as well as from small companies that make only about 300 kilos a week. The modest intentions were to show off the variety of products in Yorkshire, then we discovered that other companies wanted to join in too so they're all in the different classes. We invite judges who are independent and self-employed in the industry, buyers and retailers, graders employed by dairy companies and selectors from supermarkets. Two judges are allocated to judge appropriate classes and no, they

Jayne Hickinbotham and a traditional Cheshire cheese.

don't fall out, We haven't had a black eye yet!

There are a number of aspects that judges look out for – that little bit of extra complexity and character flavour which comes in addition to a competently made product. Those are the ones that tend to win the top prizes. Other intrinsic factors include characteristic texture, whether it is truly representative of its variety, and its shape and appearance. Balance of flavours, such as sugar and fruit, and 'mouthfeel' or coarse ice crystals become important in yoghurt and ice creams.

Competitors are allowed up to three entries of the same variety per class so the ultimate ambition is to get a first, second and third in your class. The entries are anonymous during judging – they just have a three-figure number on them.

We've got it sussed now. As the Chief Steward I have the catalogue in a sealed envelope so I'm allowed to peek if there are

any queries. The judges just go 'blind' and when all the results come in, that's when we publish the names of the exhibitors and then within about an hour and a half on Tuesday morning, all my other stewards and assistants have to put all the identity labels and prize cards on the exhibits ready for the public.

I got into the industry by accident. I did residential work with emotionally disturbed children for about eighteen months. That type of work is very demanding and I just needed a nine-to-five job while I reconsidered what I wanted to do. I happened to get a stores clerk job in a small dairy in Somerset and it's from there that the interest in the product just grew. I then got more interested in production and I worked at Wensleydale Dairy Products from 1983 to 1985. Since then I've worked in different dairies doing production and also quality. I'm a cheese grader and an accredited butter grader.

I've seen lots of dairy closures. In the

Eric Chittell ('Eric Pollard' in Emmerdale) judging an iron of Wensleydale cheese.

1990s, large dairies were buying up smaller ones, and BSE culls and quotas meant there was a shortage of milk. That shut some more and then large dairies got bigger and bigger but quietly and steadily small producers started setting up with goats and sheep and then there was enthusiasm for the specialist artisan cheese. In other words, people who have probably about eighty cows themselves or two hundred sheep. They milk those animals and they use their own milk to make dairy products and cheese. It's all done on the premises, very small scale, manually intensive, very traditional. No one who makes cheese needs a subscription to a gym.

We're planning to do a display at the show this year of a mini dairy. I've got some fifteen-inch doll dairy workers, we've also got a cow, a pasteuriser, a vat, a drainer, showing a simplified process of how to make cheese. There will also be pictures relating to the small-scale operation, the traditional method as well as pictures and diagrams of all the big automated methods of handling the cheese.

There's a very high demand for the artisan products and a lot of these people have good margins on their products – they're selling into high-quality outlets and they recognise there is an optimum size for their business. Small is beautiful. We're getting more and more people setting up to make small-scale local products.

The big dairies get bigger. For instance in the south-west, cheddar plants can make one hundred tons a day – to visualise that it's five lorry loads of cheese. Three hundred kilos is about half a pallet, which is about a fortieth of a lorry! Or three hundred bags of sugar if that makes it easier to visualise.

With dairy farmers going out of milk, we're short of milk and with the growth of the small producers and the popularity for ewe's milk and goats' milk, we haven't got enough of that either. It's not growing with the rate of demand. We're trying to look for other milk supplies – the UK produces extremely good quality microbiologically clean milk and liquid raw milk brought in from the Continent won't do the business.

A non-dairy friend of mine asked me if we were eating less cheese because she'd heard that Continental imports were dropping. I said 'No', it's because people starting up in the UK are making equivalent types of cheese. You've got some very good, very small businesses making excellent Camembert and brie-type cheeses, mostly in the south. For example, one is 'Cornwall' spelt backwards and they can't make enough. The demand is phenomenal.

The other big issue is cheddar, cheddar and more cheddar. Everybody wants to sell cheddar in the UK whether it's Canadian, Australian, New Zealand or European producers as well. So a lot of our English cheddar makers are getting very smart and getting big points of difference in flavour which is coming out on top and is fantastic. I think we're winning on quality.

When I do my day job, I do my own training courses on micro-biology, dairy hygiene, pasteurisation, cleaning and chemicals because that's very specific in dairies, as well as food safety risk analysis and grading. It's all about getting the product right and complying with the law and food standards. Food safety regulations had a big impact but our dairies were ahead of EC legislation.

I would say that the biggest burden to the small producers starting up today is that they have so much more to do in terms of paperwork, risk analysis and testing. Instead of just setting up making cheese, and then over the years developing systems and adding those aspects, it's all got to be in place when you start nowadays.

At the Great Yorkshire, we thought we'd set up with enough space – which was about the size of the top floor of my two-bedroom

Handcrafting real Yorkshire cheese at the Wensleydale Creamery, Hawes. (courtesy Wensleydale Dairy Products)

house. We thought we'd be very happy if we got about 150 entries. Then when the entries came in we had 301 and we didn't have enough table space – the tables were all bending with the weight of the cheeses. Loads of dairy producers outside of Yorkshire wanted to come too.

At the initial show we had a lot of support from the Yorkshire exhibits and it was fantastic and everybody enjoyed it and because we didn't have enough room, the Society said they would try and give us more space for the following year. Then even more people entered so we were still short of space! After a couple of years they decided to move us out of the restaurant area into a main exhibition hall. Last year we ended up with 713 entries. It's been a phenomenal growth. With our sponsors this year we have plans to extend and improve the customer information about the products.

I have a very good competent and enthusiastic group of people so I usually arrive with a team at twelve o'clock on the Sunday, set the tables up, put out all the place markings, set the fridges up, start putting up the public information and then on Monday morning all the entries come in so we have to make sure they're in the right place. Then all the judging starts so a lot of my stewards act as recorders for the judges. They have the clipboards and Biros. The judges have the cheese irons and can concentrate on judging, giving marks and comments while the stewards do the scribbling and adding up. We collate all the results and then Annie in the show office has the big job on Monday night of typing out all the results ready for the next morning.

Some of these cheeses are twenty-seven kilos – big farmhouse cheddars. Everybody assumes that all dairy products are risky for hygiene and have to go in the fridge. But cheese is naturally preserved milk – loads and loads of very nice friendly bacteria, lactic

acid, reduction of moisture, addition of salt and there we go. The cheese that's out on the tables can actually take ambient temperatures because a lot of it is pre-tested by the dairies who send it and they are matured between eight and fourteen degrees anyway. The cheeses that are on the tables, particularly the prize winners, are absolutely fine on Thursday night, just as they were when they came in on Monday morning. Probably with even more flavour on them.

Perishable products such as milks, creams, yoghurts, butter and so on are kept in the fridge as they are purposely classified as chilled products and they'd make a bit of a mess on the tables. They are judged in the fridge.

When I'm at the Great Yorkshire, I really like seeing all the livestock – all the different cattle and I've never seen so many different kinds of sheep in my life. We popped down to tell a dairy farmer that his cow had won Best Milk from an Individual Cow and discovered she'd won Best of Breed. That won't be coincidence. My partner is absolutely fascinated by the farrier competitions and the falconry and we love watching the sheep shearing. The Yorkshire Show has really kept its agricultural core of activities.

I find our part of the show important because it's becoming a social get-together for people involved in the dairy industry and a source of trusted information for the public. We link the product with the raw material. You can discuss the products, talk to the members of the public, and spread the enthusiasm for it. For me, it's like one neat project that you see from the planning stage to one that materialises in front of you. Everybody who comes – the public and people within the industry – get so much pleasure out of it and I feel that's where the satisfaction lies.

'IT'S ALWAYS THE PIGS THAT HAVE INTERESTED ME' PETER BRIER

Chief Pig Steward at the Great Yorkshire, Peter Brier is now retired. He came with his family to their eight-and-a-half acre farm at Burley-in Wharfedale in 1949 where he later farmed with his father and then with the help of his son David.

When we came up here in 1949 from Horsforth, the farm was pigs and poultry. In latter years we gradually got so busy with the pedigree side of the pigs that the poultry had to go. Then we reared a few cattle on the land but mainly pedigree pigs – we had Landrace, Large White, and towards the end we had some Durocs. I retired ten years ago and we still live in the house but we sold the buildings.

We started off years ago in Saddlebacks when I was about eight years old and I was taught to show pigs. I helped to show my first champion when I was eleven at York market. I'll never forget it – it was VJ day. My father was a butcher and farmer but he gave up the butchery business at the beginning of the war.

The first time we ever exhibited at the Great Yorkshire Show would be 1962. There was Foot & Mouth in '61 but it was all over a lot quicker than the 2001 outbreak. Foot & Mouth was in the next field to us but they didn't slaughter us out because of the

Peter Brier with some of his pigs at Burley-in-Wharfedale. [1996]

pedigree herd and at that point we'd got to be one of the top Landrace herds in the country so the Ministry didn't want to get rid of us.

That year was the last time the Royal Show roved about and it was held at Newcastle. At the Great Yorkshire, I beat the Royal's second-prize winner down to third in the senior boars with Mossbrook Hamster our senior boar at that time. This surprised me as I'd only shown at small local shows up to that time. We'd no chance of beating the Supreme Champion because he'd won championships all over and he went on to win at some shows for another year.

My first memories of the Great Yorkshire was showing in the old concrete pens where Sainsbury's is now. It was in those pens that I had my best results. We had best Landrace three years on the trot – 1976, '77, '78 – so I did the hat-trick.

You got a rapport going with the pig you were showing. If it was a senior boar, you trained him and more or less lived with him for three weeks. He knew what you were going to do and you knew what he was going to do – within reason. I remember getting pushed to the other side of a wall as we went in the ring – he went one side and I went the other and he was a lot heavier than me… but he just stood there and waited for me. He knew what he was doing.

Training can take at least a month from the start of just going in the pen when the pig's frightened of you, to getting its confidence and gradually building that up. The last ten days before the show are the most important.

Pigs' temperaments vary. There are no two pigs alike really. In the main, it depends how they're being treated. If they're looked after properly, you get rapport with them and then you're all right, it's easy enough. Some boars, some sows even, can get a little bit difficult.

When we used to do shows and sales up and down the country, we used to take a six or seven month-old boar in the ring and if I didn't have a hole in my knee after it, I hadn't had a good do!

I joined the Great Yorkshire Show Pigs Committee in '65. I've been helping out as liaison between the British Pig Association and the show since then, and have been judging since 1967. I've done almost every county show, including the Royal (twice). I only became Chief Steward at the Great Yorkshire as late as 2003.

Pig farmers are going through a very difficult time at the moment. I can't see any way out really. The basic problem is that where they were buying barley at less than £100 a ton, we're looking at nearly £200 a ton so it's doubled the cost of production. It means the majority of these people are losing £25 a pig. I know commercial people up in the East Riding, one in particular who's producing 800 pigs a week and he's losing £25 a pig. It doesn't take a lot of adding up to know that they're soon going to be out of business. They aren't physically losing it but they could have made that extra money and they aren't going to stay in pigs that long if it goes on. Even the corn growers could sell the corn at a lot better money than feeding it to pigs.

Even the pig farmers who have their own farm shops are feeling the pressure. I don't think at this minute it will make all that much difference to the entries at the Great Yorkshire because they [the competitors] are mainly small pedigree herds. Some of them are people who keep pigs for a hobby but they will be cutting their sow numbers back as well. Last year I think we had 330 entries. It will be hard to hit that target this time.

The Great Yorkshire Show have put a tremendous amount of money and work into getting the pig section as it is. It's only three years ago since we'd 180-odd entries and I managed to cut the entry price and to put the

A bowler-hatted Peter Brier judging Mixed Pairs of White Pigs at the Royal Show. [1997]

prize money up so we're actually the best show to go to. It doubled the entries overnight so really they didn't lose out on it.

The breed sections are divided into ages and sex and there are usually about five classes in each section. We have nine different breed classes and two sections for all the other breeds. Then at the Great Yorkshire we have the BPA Pig of the Year Final on the Wednesday.

I started just being able to judge Landrace. You get maybe one show every other year of judging just the one breed and then they start you on small shows. I was lucky because I was brought up with Saddlebacks, not with Landrace, so I had a knowledge of Saddlebacks as well. It was the Saddleback that we won our first championship with. So you're slowly learning about breeds.

Every judge worth his salt has a standard of excellence for each breed but basically you're all looking for the same thing. You're all looking for sound legs and sound feet, good underline and so on. You know in your mind's eye what type you're looking for in the breed. I was on the Landrace breed panel for about seven or eight years and then I was asked to go on the all breeds list.

The rare breeds are now called traditionals. There are seven traditional breeds in this country and six they now call modern breeds, mainly commercial white breeds but the majority of entries at any show now are the traditional because of the hobby people.

At the Great Yorkshire, it's always been the pigs that have interested me. It's very rare I ever get away from the pig lines really but one part I do like is the beef cattle. That interest probably comes from two generations of butchers.

In the future, we'll be looking to attract more people to show and bring in more entries. I'm still involved in the British Pig Association and eventually hope to introduce pig classes to Countryside Live held at the end of October. Here all the livestock classes are judged for the meat quality as a finished product. I organised a stand for BPA last year and had a sausage competition there and I also look forward to moving forward over the next few years.

What makes the Great Yorkshire special is the attitude of the Society. I deal with quite a lot of shows up and down the country, twelve or thirteen on a regular basis. Quite a lot of people know me and we talk about things like that. The Great Yorkshire Show are very understanding. They know the ins and outs – they've been there. The show was the

first to have its own showground, all the others travelled. If I want something from the Great Yorkshire, nine times out of ten I get what I want. They try to work with you and they work with the breeders and they do understand, whereas a lot of the shows are too strict and don't listen. They just note things if you complain and nothing's done about it. Yorkshire are different. They see it's done.

The show means a tremendous lot to me after being involved for so long. Also, I'm looking forward to building more things and carrying on. Four years ago I got involved with Countryside Days, when we have five thousand primary school children and I do the pig section. You get all sorts of questions: 'Why do pigs have curly tails?' 'Are they intelligent?'

I tell them they're pleased when they've got a curly tail. A little girl once said to me: 'If you like your pigs, why do you kill them and eat them?' I said, 'Because they aren't like your dog, you can't have a pig on your lap watching television… it has to be out in the yard.' Then I added: 'Anyway, they don't eat dogs, do they?' She said: 'They do in China!'

'One Man & His Pig' was put together at the Royal Lancashire about fifteen years ago when stockmen had nothing much to do on the Thursday afternoon, the last day of the show. One or two of the exhibitors decided for a bet to take the pigs through some obstacles. They all put a pound in the kitty and winner takes all. The main judge of the day judged them. That eventually went round one or two shows, then they decided to put things together and do it in the ring on the Thursday afternoon officially and that gathered quite a crowd.

That also then primed the idea of why don't we have Young Handlers competition, so it's all evolved from that. We had a Young Handlers' competition last year with thirteen heats, the Championship to be held at

The British Pig Association's 'Pig of the Year' Final, which takes place on the Wednesday.

Hatfield in August. I feel that this has improved showmanship amongst the young throughout the country. Competitors are in classes eight to twelve and thirteen to seventeen.

In 'One Man & His Pig' you don't always get the chance of taking your own pig in so you don't have a rapport with the pig. It can certainly be fun and games!

FROM TOP TO TOE

O r should it be head to hoof? A not entirely serious selection of photographs on which to finish this celebration of the Great Yorkshire Show.

HATS: The battered headgear on top of a cow's fringe contrasts with the elegant finery of Lady Hotham, wife of the then President. [2006]

HORNS: Highland champion Lettis of Meggermie in the cattle parade on the show's final day. [1998]

HEADS: Horses in the stables pose for the camera. [2005]

EARS: An Anglo Nubian goat – and Megan
Cromack, age 4. [2003]

EYES: A piercing look from Boris, the golden eagle
from Falconry UK Ltd at Kirby Wiske, near Thirsk.
[2004]

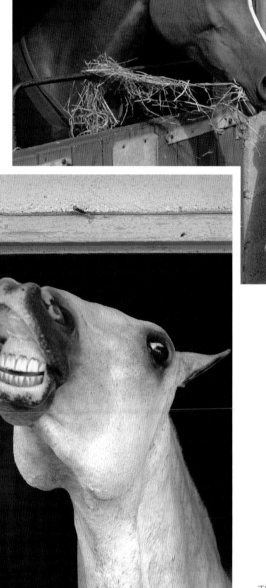

NOSES: Carl Chandler has a close encounter with a pair of large nostrils. Looking on is his grandmother Doris Chandler. [2004]

TEETH: This horse almost seems to be smiling! [2003]

TONGUES: A highland cow in the cattle parade is far from happy and is foaming at the mouth. By contrast, Ban-Carla from Stirling appears to be in ecstasy as a result of a good hosing down from model Hollie Waugh from Wakefield. Many of the men watching were probably in a similar state! [2004/2006]

BACKS: Stewards leave the main ring after the Grand Parade of Cattle. [2002]

REARS: A trio of top beef stock during the inter-breed final. [1999]

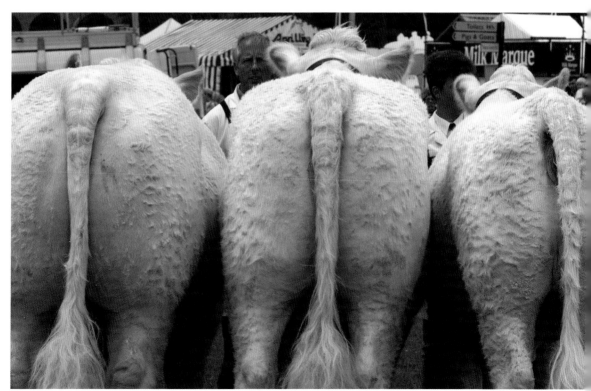

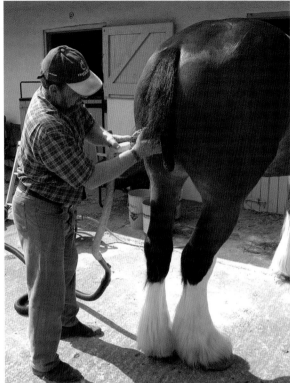

Left: TAILS: Such is the care and attention that a vacuum cleaner is brought into use! [2006]

Opposite: LEGS: Lots of them are fully displayed on the catwalk at one of the fashion shows. [2006]

Below: FEET: The hoofs of a Clydesdale horse receive attention from Colin Archibald, a Scottish exhibitor. [2004]

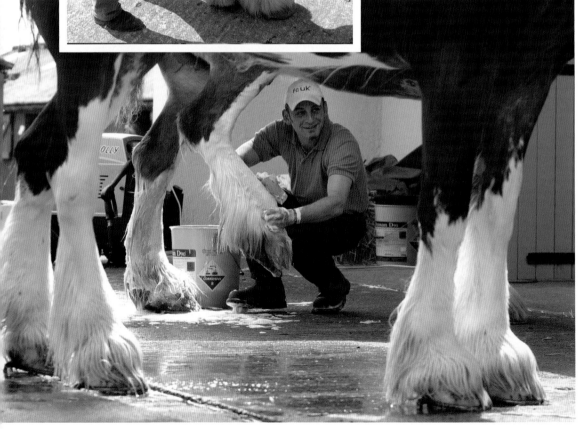

ATTENDANCE AND ENTRIES

SINCE THE SHOW CAME TO HARROGATE: ATTENDANCE SINCE 1951

* = Highest recorded attendance figure to date

Year	President	Attendance	Year	President	Attendance
2007	Michael Abrahams	122042	1977	Maj Gen J C D'A Dalton CB CBE VL	124373
2006	Lord Hotham	*135111	1976	Lord Middleton MC	121329
2005	C W Bourne-Arton	134810	1975	Christopher York DL JP	122657
2004	R E Howard-Vyse TD JP DL	124052	1974	Lord Bolton FRICS JP	119745
2003	W J Henderson FRICS DL	127152	1973	R A Bethell MFH	109019
2002	P A Smith	125793	1972	HRH The Duchess of Kent	93362
2001	Lord Gisborough	Cancelled	1971	Brig K Hargreaves CBE TD LLD	94522
2000	G T W Fenwicke-Clennell	90120	1970	F W Furness MBE	101476
1999	The Marquess of Hartington CBE	93253	1969	Maj J H A Seed TD DL JP	86402
1998	N C Forbes Adam	90466	1968	Lord St Oswald MC	95882
1997	J G Ropner DL	76544	1967	Lord Crathorne PC TD	102625
1996	R Marriott TD	79494	1966	Lt Col Sir John Dunnington-Jefferson	105554
1995	R E J Compton DL	89049		Bt DSO LLD	
1994	Lt Col H V Dawson DL	89351	1965	Sir Kenneth Parkinson	111266
1993	The Earl of Halifax JP DL	83155	1964	G R H Smith & Sir Richard Graham Bt OBE	128487
1992	The Viscount Downe DL	89284	1963	The Earl of Halifax MFH	99110
1991	Sir Marcus Worsley Bt	82558	1962	The Marquis of Normanby MBE DL	94215
1990	Maj W Warde-Aldam DL	86946	1961	Col F Lane Fox JP DL	103363
1989	Col E C York DL	92907	1960	Lord Hotham	105210
1988	Maj Gen G de E Collin CB MC DL	89196	1959	Sir William Worsley Bt	116629
1987	The Marquis of Normanby KG CBE	92243	1958	Maj Le G G W Horton-Fawkes OBE	86651
1986	Lord Martin Fitzalan Howard JP DL	94476	1957	HRH The Princess Royal	118593
1985	P S Atkinson FRICS	91573	1956	Sir William Prince-Smith Bt OBE MC	85720
1984	G F Lane Fox	100615	1955	Lord Bolton	76903
1983	Brig R Heathcoat-Amory MC	96143	1954	Sir Alfred Aykroyd Bt	80508
1982	A J Preston JP MFH	98941	1953	Lt Col Sir John Dunnington-Jefferson	
1981	L C G Gilling	110628		DSO LLD	71166
1980	The Marquess of Zetland TD DL	114067	1952	The Earl of Feversham DSO	59870
1979	Col J A M Phillips DSO MBE DL	131075	1951	HRH The Princess Royal	53979
1978	Frank K Abbey CBE	129069			

SINCE THE SHOW CAME TO HARROGATE: ENTRIES SINCE 1951

Year	Horse	Cattle	Sheep	Pigs	Goat	Pigeon	Poultry	Fox hound	Beagle	Terrier	Rabbit	Cheese	Trade Stands
2007	1982	1119	1783	357	198	643		736	186	619	1202	74	983
2006	1929	1058	1766	324	216			596	263	537	1091	713	987
2005	2096	1078	1889	304	270	441	718	749	340	550	1136	711	1031
2004	1962	1000	1581	277	220	468	676	560	393	615	1128	617	651
2003	1796	692	1441	131	285	563	726	666	292	609	1330	397	645
2002	1620	556	936	125	210	576	709	204	176	595	1066	310	665
2001						Show Cancelled: Foot & Mouth Disease							
2000	1863	859	1468	237	323	654	844	154	223	628	1192		669
1999	1707	855	1447	258	258	585	872	184	205	645	1142		667
1998	1558	886	1468	281	317	701	1054	166	181	645	1142		667
1997	1782	996	1487	242	307	758	942	146	151	588	1112		668
1996	1802	946	1499	232	254	610	1024	186	168	710	1154		685
1995	1979	958	1538	193	277	596	1007	157	126	707	1604		647
1994	2056	944	1428	240	263	745	1069	135	152	721	1048		605
1993	1874	910	1340	148	239	843	1041	187	126	773			597
1992	1864	877	1336	131	253	976	977	190	152	769			584
1991	1859	948	1258		286	756	862	196	118	796			585
1990	1768	1001	1143	197	340	909	810	152	164	802			569
1989	1853	972	1041	200	276	849	795	196	150	764			552
1988	1677	971	933	170	278	781	866	240	125	792			549
1987	1528	1086	856	202	295	718	871	169	125	739			551
1986	1397	1057	705	209	258	673	737	217	128	590			554
1985	1376	1084	740	182	227	491	745	204	108	563			552
1984	1486	1017	608	210	197	417	570	186	139	654			536
1983	1480	1009	669	153	116	549	520	187	109	648			519
1982	1515	1022	665	160	156	609	468	174	138	454			520
1981	1467	1039	638	224	171	569	527	172	116	377			510
1980	1487	1072	608	200	217	728	493	108	112	459			508
1979	1544	968	618	257	199	582	389	155	129	391			491
1978	1480	1030	600	210	181	432	242	126	89	302			499
1977	1515	917	544	133	225	498		142	124	275			492
1976	1366	971	500	129	124	531		142	103	281			500
1975	1173	903	473	60	152	645		109	120	291			484
1974	1436	907	429		122	607		112	82	317			461
1973	1403	889	414		135	674		163	103				453
1972	1257	687	420	209	156	610		119	102				441
1971	1236	702	458	236	135	567		134	88				456
1970	945	595	409	193	107	730		91	100				451
1969	1129	528	386	216	111	637		121	126				476
1968	1060	599	418	259	134	816		133	108				472
1967	876	832	460	235	120	628		123	94				466
1966	738	875	469	273	95	721		135	106				463
1965	884	860	411	295	119	725		83	104				449
1964	816	859	428	266	106	811		69	81				445
1963	762	865	416		101	727		92	64				435
1962	809	1126	406	491	94	691		74	78				434
1961	792	884	393		119	684		97	79				430
1960	729	879	405	525	117	722		66	77				410
1959	705	836	339	560	135	679		71	93				397
1958	638	814	336	460	133	609		52	67				380
1957	701	738	340	455	128	602		50	56				373
1956	741	763	324	325	109	544		56	77				373
1955	601	746	295	302	86	570		51	63				367
1954	570	618	298	327	112	530		78	66				335
1953	629	591	271		87	527	377	73	52				327
1952	602	530	290	446	120	524		53	51				320
1951	558	558	274	423	160	501		111	69				309

THE SHOW IN YORKSHIRE BEFORE 1951

Year	Place	President	Attendance
1950	Malton	The Earl of Scarborough KG	65335
1949	Wakefield	The Earl of Scarborough KG	78878
1948	Royal Show at York	Brig Gen Sir Edward N Whitley KCB CMG DSO	
1947-1940	No Show	Brig Gen Sir Edward N Whitley KCB CMG DSO	
1939	Halifax	Brig Gen Sir Edward N Whitley KCB CMG DSO	37043
1938	Doncaster	Col W St Andrew Warde-Aldam DSO	59794
1937	York	HRH The Princess Royal	70578
1936	Beverley	Lord Middleton	49864
1935	Sheffield	The Earl Fitzwilliam	50638
1934	Bradford	Sir James Hill Bt	52894
1933	Middlesbrough	The Marquess of Zetland KT	52611
1932	Leeds	Lord Irwin	49057
1931	Huddersfield	Maj L B Holliday	64396
1930	Hull	Capt T L Wickham-Boynton	44757
1929	Royal Show at Harrogate	Sir Harold Mackintosh	
1928	Halifax	Sir Harold Mackintosh	82024
1927	Darlington	Col W H A Wharton	32548
1926	Harrogate	Viscount Lascelles KG DSC	52845
1925	Bradford	Capt C S Greenwood	58198
1924	York	Lord Deramore	38212
1923	Sheffield	Lt Col E W Stanyforth CB	44391
1922	Hull	Col Sir G A Duncombe Bt	60520
1921	Leeds	Maj J W Dent LLD	65044
1920	Royal Show at Darlington	Lord Middleton	
1919–1915	No Show	The Earl of Harewood	
1914	Bradford	Walter Morrison	82461
1913	York	The Rt Hon H W Fitzwilliam	52628
1912	Royal Show at Doncaster	Lord Wenlock (to Feb 1912) The Rt Hon H W Fitzwilliam	
1911	Rotherham	The Earl Fitzwilliam	37435
1910	Leeds	The Rt Hon Rupert E Beckett	59321
1909	Beverley	Arthur Wilson	38217
1908	Halifax	Lord Savile	57976
1907	Barnsley	Viscount Halifax	46386
1906	Middlesbrough	The Marquess of Zetland KT	42952
1905	Hull	Lord Herries	49951
1904	Huddersfield	Sir John W Ramsden Bt	53407
1903	Sheffield	The Earl Fitzwilliam	54913
1902	Leeds	The Earl of Feversham	48206
1901	Bradford	Viscount Mountgarret	54439
1900	Doncaster	F Bacon Frank	20193
1899	Hull	Lord Middleton	59559
1898	Leeds	Ernest W Beckett MP	67009
1897	Harrogate	The Earl of Harewood	50925
1896	York	HRH The Duke of York KG	54692
1895	Halifax	Sir Savile B Crossley Bt	65375
1894	Beverley	Lord Herries	37186
1893	Dewsbury	Lord Savile	65266
1892	Middlesbrough	The Rt Hon James Lowther MP	59686
1891	Bradford	Lord Masham	86143
1890	Harrogate	The Earl of Harewood	59371

Year	Place	President	Attendance
1889	Hull	Arthur Wilson	76797
1888	Huddersfield	Sir John W Ramsden Bt	66249
1887	York	Lord Wenlock	31147
1886	Sheffield	The Duke of Norfolk	57082
1885	Selby	Lord Londesborough	31405
1884	Ripon	Basil T Wood	31399
1883	Royal Show at York	The Earl of Feversham	
1882	Halifax	Sir Henry Edwards Bt	59024
1881	Hull	Christopher Sykes	63580
1880	Barnsley	W T W S Stanhope	34985
1879	Leeds	Col Robert Gunter	53018
1878	Northallerton	The Rt Hon George E Lascelles	27823
1877	York	The Earl of Zetland	39412
1876	Skipton	Lord F C Cavendish	26878
1875	Driffield	W H Harrison Broadley	27149
1874	Sheffield	Lord Auckland	64111
1873	Harrogate	John Dent	30907
1872	Malton	The Earl of Feversham	30659
1871	York	Lord Wemlock	32951
1870	Wakefield	Sir Lionel Pilkington Bt	26896
1869	Beverley	George Legard	17751
1868	Wetherby	George Lane Fox	10669
1867	Thirsk	Sir George O Wombwell Bt	20576
1866	York	The Rt Hon A Duncombe	22192
1865	Doncaster	The Duke of Devonshire	20261
1864	Howden	Lord Wenlock	12827
1863	Stockton	The Earl of Zetland	15322
1862	York	H S Thompson	16054
1861	Royal Show at Leeds	The Earl of Cathcart	
1860	Pontefract	The Earl of Harewood	17259
1859	Hull	Lord Herries	22907
1858	Northallerton	Lord Bolton	11756
1857	York	Lord Greenock	12722
1856	Rotherham	Lord Wharncliffe (Aug – Oct 1855) The Earl of Effingham (Oct 1855 – Jul 1856)	13664
1855	Malton	The Earl of Carlisle	18427
1854	Ripon	The Earl de Gray	11686
1853	York	Lord Hotham	17160
1852	Sheffield	The Earl Fitzwilliam	19825
1851	Bridlington	Lord Londesborough	7799
1850	Thirsk	The Duke of Leeds	6771
1849	Leeds	The Earl of Carlisle	11780
1848	Royal Show at York	Sir J B V Johnstone Bt	
1847	Scarborough	The Earl of Harewood	7492
1846	Wakefield	Lord Wenlock	6722
1845	Beverley	The Earl of Feversham	5469
1844	Richmond	The Earl of Zetland	3410
1843	Doncaster	Lord Wharncliffe	5755
1842	York	Lord Wharncliffe	6044
1841	Hull	Lord Wharncliffe	not recorded
1840	Northallerton	The Earl Spencer	
1839	Leeds	The Earl Spencer	
1838	York	The Earl Spencer	
1837	YAS formed October in York	The Earl Spencer	

TRUEMAN'S TALES

'Fiery Fred' – Yorkshire's Cricketing Giant

By John Morgan and David Joy

With contributions from: Dickie Bird, Ian Botham, Geoffrey Boycott, Brian Close, Raymond Illingworth, Bill Pertwee and Harvey Smith.

This book began as a collaboration between Fred Trueman and David Joy in early 2006. Then came Fred's untimely death. Sports journalist, and long-time friend of Fred Trueman, John Morgan, completed the book, which became a fitting tribute to a cricketing legend.

Fully illustrated. Hardback.

BETWEEN THE TIDES

The Perilous Beauty of Morecambe Bay

By Cedric Robinson

Foreword by HRH The Duke of Edinburgh

Cedric Robinson records his 45 years as Queen's Guide to the Sands, an historic role that stretches back many centuries. In this book, Cedric describes the guided walk across Morecambe Bay, the wildlife encountered there and past tragedies on these treacherous sands. Superb colour photographs depict the Bay in all its amazing variety.

Fully illustrated. Hardback.

GREAT YORKSHIRE

A Celebration of 150 Shows

Foreword by HRH The Price of Wales

Published to mark the 150th Great Yorkshire Show in July 2008, this book celebrates a unique institution. Lavishly illustrated with archive photographs from the Yorkshire Agricultural Society and the Yorkshire Post. This large format, full colour hardback is a book to treasure.

STORM FORCE

Britain's Wildest Weather

TV weathermen Michael Fish MBE, Ian McCaskill and Paul Hudson recall the most devastating gales and ferocious floods in Britain's history

Storm Force is full of fascinating facts, extraordinary human stories, by turns amusing, inspiring, astonishing and downright weird! Beautifully produced in hardback, this is a book with many dramatic photographs that also provides an exciting read and is at the same time immensely thought provoking.

FROZEN IN TIME

The Years When Britain Shivered

Ian McCaskill and Paul Hudson remember when winters really were winters.

Using dramatic pictures and news reports from national and regional archives, recalling the worst winters ever with particular attention given to 1947, 1963 and 1979. An exciting and thought provoking read.

Fully illustrated. Hardback.

Visit www.greatnorthernbooks.co.uk